The quantum world

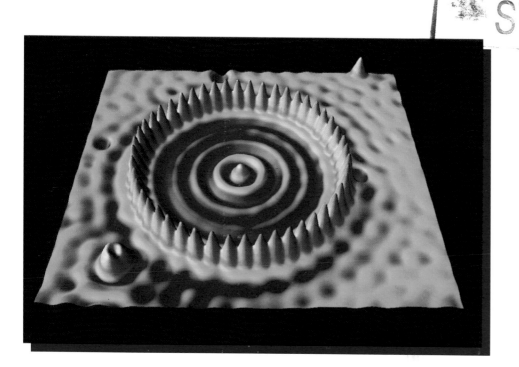

The Open University

Photo on title page   A ring of 48 iron atoms sitting on a copper surface. The image, obtained using a scanning tunnelling microscope, shows peaks where there are high densities of electrons. These in turn correspond to the locations of the atoms. The ring of atoms is only 14.3 nm in diameter, so is shown here at a magnification of about ten million times.

The Open University, Walton Hall, Milton Keynes MK7 6AA

First published 1998

Written, edited, designed and typeset by the Open University.

Printed and bound in the United Kingdom by Jarrold Book Printing, Norfolk, England.

ISBN 0 7492 8193 6

This text forms part of an Open University course, S103 *Discovering Science*. The complete list of texts that make up this course can be found on the back cover. Details of this and other Open University courses can be obtained from the Course Reservations Centre, PO Box 724, The Open University, Milton Keynes MK7 6ZS, United Kingdom: tel. (00 44) 1908 653231.

For availability of this or other course components, contact Open University Worldwide Ltd, The Berrill Building, Walton Hall, Milton Keynes MK7 6AA, United Kingdom: tel. (00 44) 1908 858585, fax (00 44) 1908 858787, e-mail ouwenq@open.ac.uk. Alternatively, much useful course information can be obtained from the Open University's website http://www.open.ac.uk

s103block7i1.1

Contents

Introduction

Over the past century, scientists have made several great voyages of discovery, but perhaps the most spectacular of them was the one in which they travelled the shortest distance. By penetrating only a tenth of a millionth of a millimetre beyond the outer edges of atoms (see the photo on the title page), scientists have uncovered a new quantum world with a host of features that no one had foretold.

In Block 6, you saw the basic picture of how atoms are built. Remember, a typical atom consists of tiny particles called electrons moving around a tiny nucleus at the core of the atom. Now, in Block 7, we shall continue the theme of 'taking the world apart' by:

* looking more closely at the electrons in atoms and finding out more about their energies and how they are arranged;

* looking inside the nucleus and finding out which combinations of protons and neutrons are stable, and how unstable combinations lead to radioactive decay;

* looking inside the protons and neutrons of the atomic nucleus to discover that they too contain other particles.

None of these areas could be tackled using the science of the late 19th century and it took a revolution in scientific thinking before scientists were equipped to tackle the problem of understanding the true nature of matter. The revolution was that of **quantum physics**, about which you will be learning a good deal in the first part of this block.

A scientific revolution is a period marked by some major discoveries that lead to a complete change in the way an area of science is approached. Can you think of any other scientific revolutions that you have met so far in S103?

Other examples are: Newton's laws that led to a new way of understanding motion both on Earth and in the Solar System (Block 3); plate tectonics that led to a revolution in our understanding of the Earth (Block 3); Darwin's theory of evolution by natural selection (Block 4) and Mendeléev's construction of the Periodic Table of the elements which revolutionized understanding of chemical processes (Block 6).

If you had told most physicists at the end of the 19th century that their branch of science was going to undergo a complete upheaval, they would probably not have believed you. At that time, there was a widespread, though not universal, complacency in the scientific community. As early as 1875, a young student by the name of Max Planck began his studies at the University of Munich, only to be encouraged by the professor of physics not to study science as there was nothing new to be discovered.

Planck (Figure 1.1) wisely ignored his professor's advice and went on to make what is now regarded as one of the most important discoveries in the entire history of science, a finding that has been fundamental to our modern understanding of atoms. His discovery concerned light or, more generally, electromagnetic radiation (Figure 1.2). You may remember from Block 2 that light is merely one kind of electromagnetic radiation and that there are many other kinds, ranging from radio waves, microwaves, and infrared radiation to ultraviolet radiation, X-rays and gamma-rays. You may also remember that these different kinds of radiation are

Figure 1.1 Max Planck (1858–1947) began the quantum revolution. His son Erwin recalled that Planck said to him during a walk in a park in late 1900: 'Today I have made a discovery which is as important as Newton's'. He was not exaggerating. On that occasion Planck introduced the first of the many concepts that now make up 'quantum physics' in an attempt to explain some of the observed properties of the light and other electromagnetic radiation given off by hot objects.

distinguished by their different *wavelengths*. Later in this block you will see that they can be distinguished by the different amounts of *energy* they carry, and by the *frequency* of the radiation as well. One aim of this block is to develop expressions for the relationships between these properties.

Figure 1.2 The electromagnetic spectrum. The divisions between the different regions of the spectrum are actually rather arbitrary — the names are merely labels that we assign to electromagnetic radiation in different ranges of wavelength.

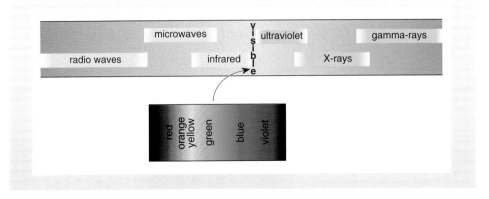

Towards the end of the 19th century, many scientists were trying to understand the properties of the radiation emitted by hot objects (Figure 1.3). As you may remember from Block 2, *all* hot objects emit electromagnetic radiation, and the amount of radiation that they produce at different wavelengths depends on the temperature of the object. For instance, the electromagnetic radiation emitted by the Earth is mainly in the form of infrared radiation, whereas that from a hotter body, such as the Sun, is mainly in the visible part of the spectrum. Some people thought this phenomenon was a minor diversion and that it would be understood using old ideas, but in it lay the seeds of a scientific revolution.

Figure 1.3 The light emitted by a hot object changes colour as the temperature of the object is raised from (a) to (d). These changes are easy to observe, but formulating a detailed theory to account for them proved to be surprisingly difficult and ultimately led to the introduction of radically new scientific concepts.

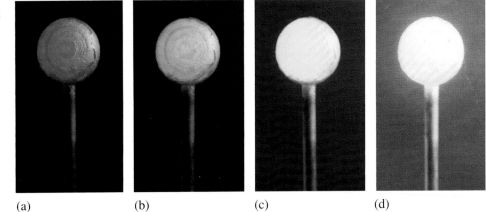

(a)　　　　(b)　　　　(c)　　　　(d)

In 1900, Planck made the astonishing suggestion that when objects emit or absorb radiation they can do so only in multiples of a certain minimum amount of energy called a **quantum** (plural quanta). So, for example, the filament inside an ordinary light bulb emits energy in the form of light, but it does not emit energy in just any amounts, rather it emits it in certain, particular amounts: quanta of light. Likewise, when light is absorbed by, say, a piece of metal (Block 2, Activity 5.1), the energy of the light is absorbed only in quanta.

The details of Planck's idea need not concern us at this stage; what is important for our purposes here is the historical significance of his idea. Planck was the first to introduce the idea of the quantum into science, but within 25 years, other scientists had used it to form the basis of quantum physics, which in turn is the basis of our current understanding of how atoms behave.

In this block, you will see how it is possible to find out about atoms and electrons by investigating how atoms absorb and emit energy in the form of quanta of radiation. Quantum physics enables us to understand this — it describes both the radiation that is emitted and absorbed, and also the atoms themselves. Indeed, without quantum physics, it would be impossible to describe either atoms or electromagnetic radiation, such as light, or their interactions.

Question 1.1   In the everyday world, the fact that objects are composed of individual atoms is not normally apparent. The reason for this is that atoms are so very small by everyday standards. Why do you think the fact that light is emitted and absorbed in discrete amounts of energy is not normally apparent either? ◀

Since the 1920s quantum physics has continued to grow and diversify. It provides insights into a vast range of phenomena, and supplies the scientific basis for many 'high-tech' industries, ranging from the manufacture of computer chips to the fabrication of the tiny lasers that are used in CD players. The 'age of information technology' could never have come about without the underpinning science of quantum physics.

Ask an astronomer why stars, such as the Sun, are able to shine so brightly, and you will learn that the answer lies ultimately in the realm of quantum physics (Figure 1.4). Ask a chemist why some atoms stick together to form molecules but others do not, or ask a biologist why DNA molecules fold up in the particular way that they do, and you will again be told that the answer ultimately lies in quantum physics. Ask almost anyone how the whole Universe came into existence and they will probably say that they haven't a clue; but if you speak to one of the small band of scientists who are actively engaged on this problem they will tell you that their best bet is that it involves quantum physics in some fundamental way.

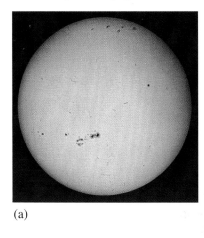
(a)

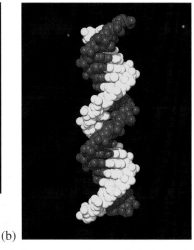
(b)

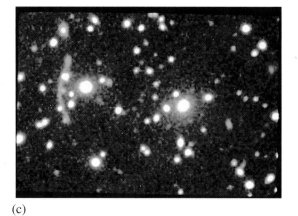
(c)

Figure 1.4   Quantum physics is needed to account for: (a) light from the Sun; (b) the highly coiled structure of a DNA molecule, responsible for carrying genetic information; (c) a collection of distant galaxies stretching half way to the edge of the visible Universe.

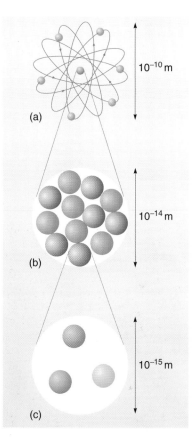

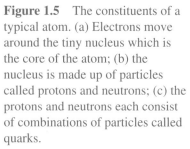

Figure 1.5 The constituents of a typical atom. (a) Electrons move around the tiny nucleus which is the core of the atom; (b) the nucleus is made up of particles called protons and neutrons; (c) the protons and neutrons each consist of combinations of particles called quarks.

The cosmic significance of quantum physics will be discussed in Block 11, where it will provide a suitable finale to the process of *discovering science*. For the moment however, in this block, our aims are simpler and more modest. In particular, we want to achieve the following:

1   In Sections 2 and 3, we will introduce you to some of the phenomena that distinguish quantum physics from the physics that preceded it, such as Newton's laws. Quantum physics, like intelligent life, is hard to define but fairly easy to recognize. Sections 2 and 3 will show you why.

2   In Sections 4, 5 and 6, you will see how quantum physics clarifies the current scientific picture of the fundamental structure of matter (see Figure 1.5). To this end, Section 4 treats *atoms* as arrangements of *nuclei* and *electrons*, Section 5 treats nuclei as arrangements of *nucleons* (i.e. *protons* and *neutrons*), and Section 6 treats nucleons as arrangements of more truly 'fundamental' particles called *quarks*. As far as matter is concerned, these three steps take us to the most fundamental level so far uncovered in the scientific process of 'taking the world apart'.

3   In Sections 7, 8 and 9, you will be introduced to the quantum physics of light, and other electromagnetic radiation. Section 8 describes how electromagnetic radiation travels from place to place as if it were a wave, whilst Section 9 shows that it interacts with matter as if it were a stream of particles.

4   In Section 10, we look briefly at the quantum nature of matter and radiation and we reach the conclusion that *both* can behave like waves or like particles, as the situation dictates.

This is quite an itinerary for your journey into the heart of the atom. During your study of this block, you will be working in the tiny, subatomic domain and will be coming to terms with ideas that are almost unbelievable in the context of the everyday world. Most people are awe-struck by spectacles such as mountain scenery here on Earth or an exploding star in outer space. Prepare yourself to encounter phenomena that are much too small for you to be able to see but that are nonetheless fascinating and mysterious.

You may think that much of what you will be learning in this block defies common sense. If so, you may be right. But then again, perhaps Einstein had a point when he remarked that 'common sense is the deposit of prejudice laid down in the mind before the age of eighteen'.

Quantized energy

One of the most revealing ways of investigating atoms is to look at how they interact with light. By examining both the light *emitted* by atoms and the light they *absorb*, scientists have been able to draw up an astonishingly detailed picture of how the electrons in atoms are arranged. In this section you will see that atoms are *characterized* by the light they emit and absorb and that, from the energies of this light, we can work out the possible values of energy that the atom can have. Note, we are concentrating on light (visible radiation) in this section, but the principles involved apply to all forms of electromagnetic radiation.

2.1 Atoms and their spectra

It was Isaac Newton who showed that when a beam of white light from the Sun is passed through a glass prism it is broken up, or dispersed, into a range of colours that form a pattern similar to a miniature rainbow (see Figure 2.1). Such a band of colours is referred to as a **spectrum** (plural spectra). Later, in Section 10, you will examine for yourself the spectrum of the white light from a conventional light bulb. You will see that it comprises an uninterrupted band of colours known as a **continuous spectrum**, such as that shown in Figure 2.2a.

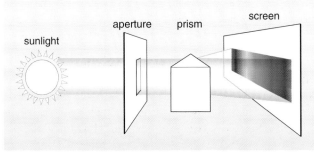

(a)

(b)

Figure 2.1 (a) Using a glass prism to show the spectrum of a beam of white light. In Section 10 you will be asked to carry out a similar experiment, but you will use a device called a diffraction grating rather than a prism to disperse the light into its different colours. (b) A naturally occurring spectrum — a rainbow. Here the light from the Sun is dispersed by passing through raindrops.

Colour, then, is a property of light itself and for most of us, it would be hard to imagine the world in shades of grey. We are used to seeing colour all around us — green leaves, blue skies, multi-coloured plants and animals, and so on. But why should things have colour? Why should the petal of one flower appear yellow, while another appears blue? The answer lies ultimately in the way light interacts with atoms.

It's not that atoms themselves are coloured, but rather that atoms and molecules absorb and emit light. Furthermore, each of the hundred or so different kinds of atom shows a preference for absorbing or emitting light of certain specific colours. Thus, just as every human being has his or her own set of characteristic fingerprints, so every type of atom (or each chemical element, if you prefer) has its own associated pattern of colours of light that it can absorb or emit — a sort of technicolour fingerprint.

○ Can you think why a leaf appears green when illuminated by white light?

○ The atoms and molecules of which the leaf is made absorb all the colours that comprise white light *except* for the green light. Some of the green light passes through the leaf, but most is reflected back from its surface, making the leaf appear green to our eyes.

This association between a specific type of atom and a limited range of colours is evident from everyday life. You are probably familiar, for instance, with the yellow glow produced by 'sodium' street lights when an electric current passes through vaporized sodium, and you may be familiar with the bright orange-red light of a neon sign. Such associations are even more apparent when a glass prism is used, in an arrangement similar to that of Figure 2.1a, to disperse the light from a source of known chemical composition.

If you were to do this using a beam of light from a yellow sodium lamp, you would find that the resulting spectrum is dominated by a bright yellow line, as shown in Figure 2.2b. This line is an example of a **spectral line**, and is a tell-tale visual fingerprint of the sodium atom. Since the light that is responsible for the line is *emitted* by sodium atoms, the spectrum as a whole is called the **emission spectrum** of sodium, and the yellow spectral line that it contains is called an **emission line**.

Figure 2.2 (a) A continuous spectrum from a beam of white light. (b) The emission spectrum of sodium. Note that this illustrates only the visible spectrum: sodium atoms also emit radiation that is not visible (e.g. infrared and ultraviolet radiation — see the electromagnetic spectrum in Figure 1.2). (c) The absorption spectrum of sodium in the visible part of the electromagnetic spectrum.

(a)

(b)

(c)

So the association between sodium and the precise shade of yellow light that characterizes it can be determined by examining the light emitted by sodium atoms. Exactly the same association may be seen by observing how white light is *absorbed* by sodium atoms. This is done by passing a beam of white light through some sodium vapour (Figure 2.3) and examining the spectrum of the emerging beam to see if any colours are missing. Figure 2.2c shows the resulting **absorption spectrum** of

Figure 2.3 Observing the effect of absorption by sodium vapour on a beam of white light.

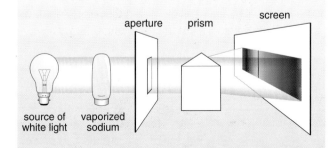

sodium; as you can see it exhibits a dark **absorption line**, marking the absence (due to absorption by the sodium vapour) of exactly the same shade of yellow that was seen in the emission spectrum (Figure 2.2b).

Sodium atoms are by no means unique in having a characteristic pattern of spectral lines. In fact, every kind of atom has an associated, characteristic 'spectral fingerprint'. Figure 2.4 shows the visible emission spectra of a few common chemical elements. In each case the light being examined originates from a lamp that contains a huge number of atoms of the relevant type, and the observed spectrum is characteristic of every atom of that type. For this reason, the kind of emission spectra shown in Figure 2.4 are often called **atomic spectra**.

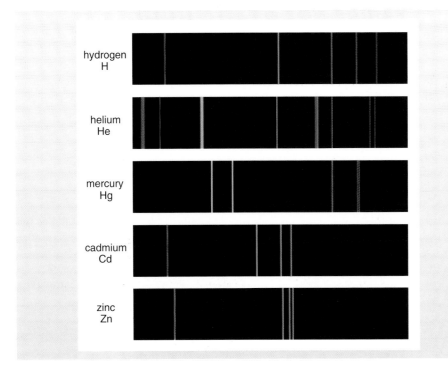

Figure 2.4   The emission spectra that characterize a number of common atoms (hydrogen, helium, mercury, cadmium and zinc). Note that only the visible part of the electromagnetic spectrum for each atom is shown here: all these atoms also emit radiation that is not visible.

The fact that atoms have 'spectral fingerprints' of the kind shown in Figure 2.4 has proved to be extremely useful to scientists. Long before the origin of such atomic spectra had been explained, scientists were using them to identify the chemical composition of vapours and flames. The basic idea is that if you observe the spectral fingerprint of an atom in some situation, you can be sure that the atom is present, much as a criminal investigator uses fingerprints left at the scene of a crime to rule in or out the possibility that a suspect was present when the deed was done.

Question 2.1   White light is passed through a certain vapour whose composition is unknown. The absorption spectrum of the light that emerges from the gas is shown in Figure 2.5. By comparing Figure 2.5 with Figure 2.4, what is the unknown gas? ◀

Figure 2.5   The absorption spectrum of the 'unknown' vapour referred to in Question 2.1.

This technique is particularly useful for scientists who are observing matter at a great distance, for example in stars and galaxies. One famous example was the discovery of the chemical element helium which was first observed not on Earth but on the Sun via its tell-tale spectral fingerprint. The key observation was made in 1868 by the astronomer Norman Lockyer, who observed a previously unknown absorption line in the spectrum of sunlight, using a telescope on Earth. He suggested that this evidence pointed to the existence of an element that had not been detected on Earth and which he named helium (after the Greek *helios*, meaning Sun). So difficult was it to detect this element on Earth that confirmation that helium actually existed on our planet had to wait another 27 years.

In view of the importance of atomic spectra, it is not surprising that explaining their origin should have been perceived as a matter of crucial scientific importance. By 1910, or so, it was obvious that the explanation involved the inner workings of the atom. It was also becoming clear, at least to some, that the then prevailing view of the structure of atoms was incapable of accounting for the observed spectral lines. It was this need to account for spectra in terms of atomic behaviour that inspired several key developments in quantum physics.

2.2 Quantum energies and photons

As light travels from place to place, it carries energy. You will remember that the energy carried by radiation from the Sun played a vital part in our discussion of the Earth's surface temperature in Block 2. For centuries, scientists believed that the energy of light could be transferred in arbitrary amounts — this is just common sense, after all: why should there be any restrictions on the amounts of energy transferred by light? Yet, as you saw in Section 1, this common-sense view is wrong. As Max Planck was the first to suggest, when electromagnetic radiation is absorbed (or emitted) the energy that it delivers (or carries away) is transferred only in multiples of a certain minimum amount of energy called a quantum.

The idea of the quantum applies to all types of electromagnetic radiation, from radio waves and microwaves to X-rays and gamma-rays. But for the moment we shall concentrate on light, simply because it's easier to visualize.

What is the energy of a quantum of light? Quite simply, the answer depends on the *colour* of the light: in terms of the colours of the rainbow, quanta of red light have the lowest energy, whereas those of violet light have the highest energy. This link between colour and energy may be appreciated from Figure 1.3. There you can see that the colour of the light emitted by a hot object shifts from red to orange to yellow as the temperature increases. Recall from Block 5 that temperature is a measure of the *internal energy* of an object. So, as you increase the temperature of an object, its internal energy increases. As a result of this, the energy of the typical quanta that the object emits also increases, corresponding to a shift in colour from red to yellow, for instance.

Light of just one colour is said to be **monochromatic**, from the Greek words *mono* 'single' and *chroma* 'colour'. A quantum of monochromatic light will have a definite, fixed energy, determined by its colour. It is quite straightforward to calculate the energy of each light quantum, but we shall leave that calculation until Section 9, and for now simply state the results.

⬤ What is the conventional SI unit of energy?

◯ From Block 5, recall that energy is measured in joules, represented by the symbol J.

The value of the energy, in joules, corresponding to quanta of each of the colours of the rainbow, is indicated by the energy scale beneath the continuous spectrum in Figure 2.6. You can see that the energies corresponding to the visible part of the spectrum are characterized by rather cumbersome numbers, when expressed in joules. Box 2.1, *Electronvolts*, introduces a unit of energy that is better suited to discussions of light and atoms.

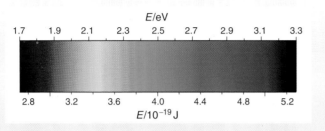

Figure 2.6 A continuous spectrum of visible radiation. The energy of quanta of light corresponding to different colours can be determined using the energy scales shown above (in electronvolts) and below (in joules) the spectrum.

Box 2.1 Electronvolts

Physicists and chemists find it very convenient to express energies of light quanta in a unit called the **electronvolt**, represented by the symbol eV (pronounced as 'ee-Vee'). One eV is the energy converted when one electron moves from one terminal of a one volt battery to the other. From Block 5 you know that when a charge Q moves through a voltage difference ΔV, the energy transfer in joules is the number of coulombs of charge transferred times the voltage difference, $\Delta E_e = Q\Delta V$. So,

$\quad$ 1 eV = (magnitude of charge on one electron) × (one volt)

$\qquad$ = $(1.6 \times 10^{-19}\,\text{C}) \times (1\,\text{V})$

$\qquad$ = $1.6 \times 10^{-19}\,\text{J}$

The following question will help to familiarize you with the use of electronvolts and will also show you why it is such a useful unit of energy when discussing light.

Question 2.2 Quanta of green light have an energy of about 3.8×10^{-19} J. What is the value of this energy when expressed in terms of electronvolts rather than joules? ◄

Like any SI unit, we can prefix eV with various multiples. So, 1 keV (one kiloelectronvolt) is 10^3 eV, 1 MeV (one megaelectronvolt) is 10^6 eV, and 1 GeV (one gigaelectronvolt) is 10^9 eV. You will see later in the block that such energies are appropriate when we deal with nuclei and quarks.

As illustrated by the answer to Question 2.2, the electronvolt is a very convenient unit because it reduces the need to use cumbersome powers of ten notation when discussing the energies of light quanta. Figure 2.6 also shows the energies of quanta of light in electronvolts — they range from around 2 eV to around 3 eV. Just as you wouldn't think of measuring the length of one of your little fingers in kilometres, atomic scientists don't normally use the joule to measure the energy of quanta, it is simply too big a unit.

It was Albert Einstein (Figure 2.7) who did most to clarify the quantum physics of light (or, more generally, of electromagnetic radiation). Although best known for his theory of relativity, arguably his most revolutionary work concerned his interpretation of quanta of light. He suggested a reason for the existence of an energy quantum corresponding to each colour in the spectrum. Einstein proposed that light of any specific colour consists of identical *particles*, each of which has an amount of energy exactly equal to the corresponding quantum of energy that is transferred when light is absorbed or emitted.

Einstein argued as follows: if the absorption or emission of light involves these particles, and if it is only possible to absorb or emit whole numbers of them, then it is inevitable that energy must always be transferred between light and matter in whole-number multiples of the relevant quantum of energy. The 'particles of light' or, more generally, 'particles of radiation' that Einstein introduced are now called simply **photons**. The concept of the photon is of such crucial importance to what follows that it deserves some emphasis.

Figure 2.7 Albert Einstein (1879–1955) has come to epitomize scientific genius. Although he was one of the founders of quantum physics — he may be thought of as the discoverer of the particle we now call the photon — he developed a strong dislike for some of its later developments. Some of his more philosophical concerns about the foundations of the subject are still shared by present-day scientists, but his doubts over the ability of quantum physics to predict correctly the outcomes of experiments have been shown to be ill-founded.

A photon is a particle of electromagnetic radiation. Monochromatic light, which has a single colour, consists of identical photons that each have exactly the same energy. The amount of energy carried by a single photon is called a quantum.

The most important thing about photons for our purposes is their energies. Figure 2.8 shows the photon energies of all the types of radiation in the electromagnetic spectrum. As you can see, the range of photon energies is huge: for example, the X-ray photons used in radiography have at least a thousand times the energy of photons of light.

○ Which carries more energy, a photon of infrared radiation or a photon of ultraviolet radiation?

○ From Figure 2.8, you can see that the photon energy increases from left to right as the spectrum is represented here. So a photon of ultraviolet radiation (with energy in the range from about $3\,\text{eV}$ to about a thousand eV) carries more energy than a photon of infrared radiation (with energy in the range from about $10^{-3}\,\text{eV}$ to about $2\,\text{eV}$).

Question 2.3 (a) A microwave oven cooks food by bombarding it with photons of microwave radiation. Roughly what is the energy of each of these photons in joules?

(b) During a dental X-ray, a patient is exposed to X-ray photons. Roughly what is the energy of each of these photons in electronvolts? ◀

Figure 2.8 The electromagnetic spectrum with photon energy scales in joules and electronvolts. Note that because the range of photon energies is so large we have used a so-called powers of ten scale; the energy changes by a factor of ten for each division along the scale. Also note that this figure is shown so that energy increases from left to right. This is the reverse of the way it was displayed in Block 2.

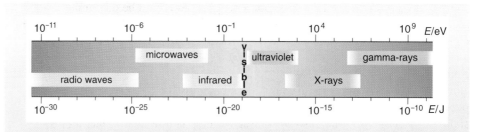

What can photons tell us about the inner workings of an atom? Well, each spectral line involves the emission or absorption of photons of a particular energy. So it follows that if we want to explain why each type of atom is associated with a particular set of spectral lines, what we really need to explain is why each type of atom only emits or absorbs photons that have certain fixed amounts of energy. These photon energies are just as characteristic of a given type of atom as the pattern of spectral lines to which they correspond. This, too, deserves emphasis.

> Each type of atom can be characterized by the energies of the photons that it can absorb or emit.

The message, then, is simple: every atom has a spectral fingerprint which can be specified in terms of either:

- the colours of the light it emits or absorbs;

or, more precisely,

- the energies of the photons it emits or absorbs.

Let us now apply these ideas to the simplest atom of all, the hydrogen atom.

2.3   The spectral fingerprint of hydrogen

You saw in Block 6 (Section 14) that every hydrogen atom consists of only a single electron moving around a proton. Our strategy in focusing on hydrogen is to examine this simplest possible atom in the confident hope that, by understanding it, we shall gain deeper insights into larger, and therefore more complex, atoms. This is standard practice in science: if you are studying something, it is almost always a good idea to begin by coming to terms with the simplest case, before moving on to investigate more complicated examples. Normally, insights from simpler cases make it easier to see 'the wood for the trees' when dealing with the messy complexities of harder situations.

So let us take a closer look at the spectral fingerprint of hydrogen atoms.

Question 2.4   The hydrogen emission spectrum shown in Figure 2.4 contains five visible lines that characterize the hydrogen atom. Using the energy scale from Figure 2.6, estimate the five corresponding photon energies (in electronvolts) that also characterize the hydrogen atom. ◄

What do the five spectral lines in the visible part of the spectrum tell us about the hydrogen atom? Well, you have just seen that the spectral fingerprint of hydrogen atoms can be specified by five particular energies, which can be determined accurately by experiment to be 1.89 eV, 2.55 eV, 2.86 eV, 3.02 eV and 3.12 eV, when expressed to three significant figures. This set of energy values represents the fact that hydrogen atoms emit light only with these five values of energy (likewise, they can absorb light only with these five energy values). So, for example, a hydrogen atom can emit a photon with an energy of exactly 1.89 eV, but can never emit a photon with an energy of, say, 1.91 eV. The hydrogen atom, then, is very selective about the light it emits and absorbs. The same thing is true for all other atoms — every type of atom can emit or absorb photons with only particular values of energy.

2.4 The energy of an atom

You saw in Block 5 that energy is always conserved. This implies that if an atom *absorbs* a photon that has a given energy, then the energy of that atom must *increase* by the same amount of energy (the energy cannot disappear). Similarly, if an atom *emits* a photon of a particular energy, then the energy of that atom must *decrease* by the same amount of energy. Thus, the fact that a given type of atom (hydrogen or helium or whatever) can absorb and emit photons of certain precisely defined energies must mean that the atoms themselves are able to increase and decrease their own energy by exactly those amounts.

Question 2.5   (a) A helium atom absorbs a photon of energy 2.11 eV. What happens to the energy of the helium atom as a result?

(b) A mercury atom emits a photon of energy 2.27 eV. What happens to the energy of the mercury atom as a result? ◄

So what is the energy of an atom? First, we're *not* talking here about the kinetic energy of the atom as a whole. The atom may well be moving, and so possess a certain amount of kinetic energy, but it is not changes in this energy that are responsible for atomic spectra. Rather we're concerned with what may be thought of as the *internal energy* of the atom. Recall from Block 5 that the internal energy of a liquid, say, has two components: the *kinetic energy* of the random motion of the constituent molecules and their *potential energy* that results from the molecular forces of attraction between the molecules. A similar situation applies in the case of individual atoms. The simplest case, a hydrogen atom, consists of a single electron moving around a central proton. The electron will have a certain amount of kinetic energy (because it is moving) and there will be a certain amount of electrical energy due to the electrical force of attraction between the negatively charged electron and the positively charged proton. The energy of the atom is the sum of these two contributions.

Now, think about what will happen if the electron in a hydrogen atom is moved further away from the proton. In Block 5 you saw that as an object is raised above the surface of the Earth, work is done against the gravitational force of attraction between the object and the Earth. As a consequence of this, the object acquires increased gravitational energy. Here, as the electron is moved further from the proton, work is done against the electrical force of attraction between the two. So in this case, there is an increase in *electrical* energy. At the same time, when an electron is moved further from the proton it will generally move more slowly, so its *kinetic* energy will decrease. In fact, it can be shown that the magnitude of the electrical energy is generally larger than that of the kinetic energy, so the electrical energy dominates the energy of the atom. In general therefore, the further away the electron is from the proton in a hydrogen atom, the greater will be the energy of the atom.

So when a hydrogen atom absorbs or emits photons, the energy of the atom will alter and changes will occur to the internal structure of the atom. In particular, the location and speed of the electron will change. When a photon is *absorbed*, the location and speed of the electron will change such that the atom has a *higher* energy, and when a photon is *emitted*, the location and speed of the electron will change such that the atom has a *lower* energy. As you will see in Section 3, the whole question of the location and speed of an electron in an atom is subject to so-called quantum indeterminacy so the picture outlined above is only a model of the true situation. Nonetheless it is a useful one to bear in mind, and similar conclusions apply to more complex atoms.

2.5   Energy levels and transitions

What does all this tell us about the structure of atoms? This was the problem that scientists had to tackle in the early years of the 20th century: how could they explain why each type of atom has its own spectral fingerprint? The solution that eventually emerged involved an extension to Planck's original quantum hypothesis and therefore marked another milestone in the quantum revolution.

The ability of any given type of atom to absorb or emit only certain characteristic amounts of energy is explained by saying that the atom itself can have only certain values of energy, known as **energy levels**. The energy is said to be *quantized*, since the energy levels correspond to only certain, well defined, values of energy. An atom with a particular value of energy, corresponding to a certain energy level, can change to another energy level by absorbing or emitting a photon (there are other ways, too, for example by colliding with other atoms) and since energy is conserved, the energy of the photon is precisely equal to the energy difference between the two energy levels. When the atom makes such a change, we say that it undergoes a **transition** to a different energy level. Such transitions are often informally referred to as *quantum jumps*. This is the key feature of the quantum world of atoms.

> When atoms emit or absorb photons, they make transitions between quantized energy levels.

The two basic types of transition — photon absorption and photon emission — are illustrated in Figure 2.9. This figure introduces the way that energy levels are represented diagrammatically, and you should study this carefully.

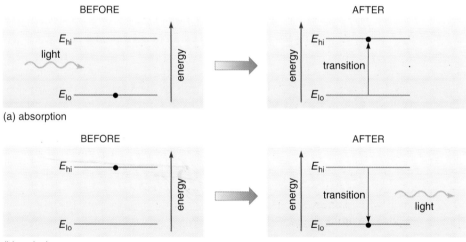

(a) absorption

(b) emission

Figure 2.9   The two horizontal lines labelled E_{hi} and E_{lo} in each part of this figure represent two of the possible energies of an atom — two of the possible energy levels. When the atom has a particular value of energy corresponding to a certain energy level, the energy level is marked with a dot. (The width of the horizontal lines in this diagram is of no significance.) (a) Absorption of a photon. The atom is initially in the lower energy level E_{lo}; it then absorbs a passing photon and makes a transition to the higher energy level E_{hi}. The photon's energy matches precisely the difference between E_{hi} and E_{lo}. (b) Emission of a photon. Here the atom is initially in the higher level E_{hi}; it emits a photon and makes a transition to the lower level E_{lo}. Again the photon's energy matches precisely the difference between E_{hi} and E_{lo}.

The emission and absorption spectra that you saw earlier in this section arise simply as a result of these transitions between energy levels. When a large number of sodium atoms, for instance, make transitions from a certain high energy level (let's call it E_{hi}) to a certain *lower* energy level (say, E_{lo}) as illustrated in Figure 2.9b, photons of a particular energy are *emitted*, and the spectrum of these photons is shown in Figure 2.2b. When white light is directed at a large number of sodium atoms, some of them will make transitions from a certain low energy level (E_{lo}) to a certain *higher* energy level (E_{hi}), and photons of a particular energy are *absorbed*, as illustrated in Figure 2.9a. The spectrum that results is shown in Figure 2.2c.

Now, the numerical value of the energy of an atom that corresponds to each energy level (E_{hi} or E_{lo} in the example above) is not generally known. Rather it is the *differences* in energies between *pairs* of levels that are well defined, since it is these differences that correspond to the energies of the photons that the atom may absorb or emit. We can summarize this by saying that when an atom absorbs a photon:

$$\left(\begin{array}{c} \text{initial lower} \\ \text{energy level} \end{array} \right) + \left(\begin{array}{c} \text{energy of} \\ \text{absorbed photon} \end{array} \right) = \left(\begin{array}{c} \text{final higher} \\ \text{energy level} \end{array} \right)$$

and when an atom emits a photon:

$$\left(\begin{array}{c} \text{initial higher} \\ \text{energy level} \end{array} \right) - \left(\begin{array}{c} \text{energy of} \\ \text{emitted photon} \end{array} \right) = \left(\begin{array}{c} \text{final lower} \\ \text{energy level} \end{array} \right)$$

Thus, in any transition where a photon is absorbed or emitted:

$$\left(\text{photon energy} \right) = \left(\begin{array}{c} \text{higher} \\ \text{energy level} \end{array} \right) - \left(\begin{array}{c} \text{lower} \\ \text{energy level} \end{array} \right)$$

or in symbols:

$$E_{ph} = \Delta E_{atom} \qquad\qquad (2.1)$$

where E_{ph} is the energy of the photon and ΔE_{atom} is the *change* in energy of the atom. (Recall from Block 5 that the Greek letter delta Δ is used to represent the *change* in a given quantity.)

Question 2.6   What is the energy of the photons emitted or absorbed by the sodium atoms when transitions take place between the energy levels E_{hi} and E_{lo} referred to above? ◀

In the case of sodium atoms, the two energy levels involved in the emission or absorption of the yellow line in the spectrum are separated by an energy difference of 2.1 eV. So the energy of the photons of yellow light in the sodium spectrum is 2.1 eV.

2.6   The energy levels of the hydrogen atom

Now let us return to the hydrogen atom. Remember, our immediate aim is to use the atom's spectral fingerprint — the energies of the light that it can emit and absorb — to find out about the energy of the atom itself.

You have seen that hydrogen atoms emit and absorb photons of just five particular energies: 1.89 eV, 2.55 eV, 2.86 eV, 3.02 eV and 3.12 eV. It is important to remember that these are only the visible lines — hydrogen also emits and absorbs radiation that is not visible, for example in the infrared and ultraviolet regions of the electro-magnetic spectrum. In order to build up a complete picture of the energy levels of the hydrogen atom, you would need a complete list of all the energies of the photons that it can emit or absorb.

Scientists have indeed produced such a list and it enables us to draw the complete **energy-level diagram** for the hydrogen atom (Figure 2.10) in which the energy values are illustrated in a conventional and convenient way. What matters here is the vertical separation of the energy levels; neither the horizontal extent of the lines nor their thickness is of any significance whatsoever. One important thing to notice about this energy-level diagram is its simplicity: the pattern is one in which the difference between successive energy levels gets smaller and smaller. As you can see from Figure 2.10, the higher energy levels of hydrogen become so densely packed that it becomes impossible to draw them as distinct lines and the best that an illustrator can do is to indicate that the lines gradually get closer and closer together. The energy-level diagram for hydrogen is in fact the simplest of all atomic energy-level diagrams, just as we might have supposed. Remember, we are studying hydrogen because it is the simplest atom of all in the hope that it would be easy to understand. Our faith has been vindicated.

As you can see from Figure 2.10, the unknown energies of the various levels are identified only by the symbols E_1, E_2, E_3, etc., but the relative separations are drawn to scale, so that each of the photon energies that was associated with hydrogen in Question 2.4 is represented by the distance *between* two energy levels. For instance, photons of visible radiation (often called simply visible photons) with the *lowest* energy (1.89 eV) are associated with transitions between energy levels E_2 and E_3, whereas the visible photons with the *highest* energy (3.12 eV) are associated with transitions between E_2 and E_7. More widely separated levels indicate transitions of relatively large energy and so photons associated with these transitions may correspond to the ultraviolet part of the spectrum (energy differences greater than about 3.2 eV). Conversely, closely separated levels indicate transitions of relatively small energy and so photons associated with these transitions may correspond to the infrared part of the spectrum (energy differences less than about 1.8 eV). Remember, transitions don't just occur between adjacent energy levels, but between *any* pair of energy levels.

Question 2.7   (a) Suppose a hydrogen atom undergoes a transition that causes its energy level to change from E_3 to E_4. In terms of these symbols, what would be the energy of the associated photon? Would the photon be absorbed or emitted?

(b) Now consider a transition that causes the energy level of a hydrogen atom to change from E_2 to E_1. In terms of these symbols, what would be the energy of the associated photon in this case? Would the photon be absorbed or emitted?

(c) A hydrogen atom makes a transition from E_7 to E_1. Bearing in mind the size of this jump when compared with those which produce visible photons, is the emitted photon in this case in the visible region of the spectrum?

(d) By absorbing a photon, a hydrogen atom makes a transition from E_5 to E_6. Bearing in mind the size of this jump when compared with those which produce visible photons, is the absorbed photon in this case in the visible region of the spectrum? ◀

Question 2.8   Figure 2.4 showed the visible emission spectrum of helium. The brightest lines in its spectrum comprise photons with energies 1.76 eV, 2.11 eV and 2.77 eV. What can you deduce from this about the energy-level diagram for helium? For example, can you deduce the values of energy corresponding to any of its energy levels? ◀

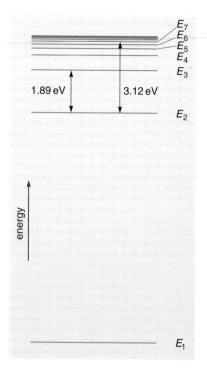

Figure 2.10   The energy-level diagram of hydrogen. Energy increases moving up this diagram. The *differences* between energy levels represent the energies of photons that may be absorbed or emitted by hydrogen atoms. Two particular energy differences are shown, and the photons emitted or absorbed when hydrogen atoms make transitions between these energy levels correspond to the red line and one of the violet lines in the visible part of the spectrum of hydrogen.

Figure 2.11 The energy-level diagram of hydrogen with some additional labels which are explained in the text.

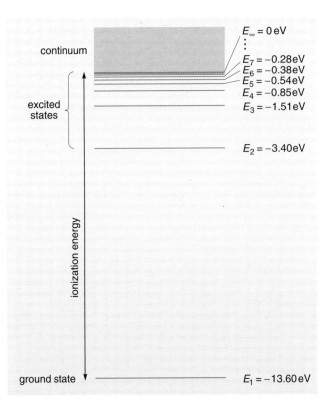

Now, let's look at the hydrogen energy-level diagram more closely. There is a lot to be learned from it and all the lessons apply to other atoms. Figure 2.11 repeats the pattern shown in Figure 2.10, with some additional labelling.

When a hydrogen atom (or in fact any other atom) has the *lowest* energy level, labelled E_1, it is said to be in its **ground state**. This is the 'normal' state in which an atom might be found. It will correspond to a situation in which the electron is likely to be close to the proton, with a minimum value of electrical energy. Above this energy, when the atom has energy E_2, E_3, E_4 and so on, it is said to be in an **excited state**. The topmost energy level is labelled E_∞, where the ∞ symbol is a mathematical shorthand that indicates 'infinity'. (Infinity is actually a difficult mathematical concept, but you can think of it simply as being greater than any other number you care to name.) This topmost energy level will correspond to a situation in which the electron and proton are widely separated, with a maximum value of electrical energy.

The next point to note is that although Figure 2.11 indicates an infinite number of levels there is still only a finite difference in energy between the lowest energy level (E_1) and the highest (E_∞). This shows that there is a limit to the amount of energy that a hydrogen atom can absorb without the electron and proton being split apart. If the atom is initially in its ground state, E_1, and it absorbs a photon with an energy greater than the difference ($E_\infty - E_1$), the electron is freed completely from its bondage to the proton at the core of the atom (the nucleus). In Block 6, you saw that the removal of an electron from a hydrogen atom leaves a charged particle which is written H^+ and is called an ion. (In fact the hydrogen ion is simply a proton.) The technical term for such removal of an electron from an atom is therefore **ionization**. The energy difference ($E_\infty - E_1$) is called the **ionization energy**, which in the case of hydrogen is measured to be 13.60 eV.

There is a continuous range of possible energies above the ionization energy and this is generally referred to as the **continuum**. It is shown in Figure 2.11 as a continuous 'band' stretching upward from E_∞. The continuum corresponds to situations in which the electron and proton move around separately, with a combined kinetic energy that is greater than E_∞. The electron is no longer bound to the proton, and the particles can have *any* value of energy.

○ A photon with energy 15 eV is absorbed by a hydrogen atom in its ground state. What happens to the atom?

○ The first 13.60 eV is used to ionize the atom, i.e. to separate completely the electron from the hydrogen nucleus, leaving 1.40 eV to be imparted to the liberated particles as kinetic energy. So, after the absorption, the result is that the electron and proton have a total energy of 1.40 eV.

Now for a rather subtle point. You have already seen that the energies of the levels are not really known. However, there is no such doubt about the *differences* in energy between the levels. These differences are very well defined, and, as you have already seen, they can be determined quite simply from atomic spectra. This means that if you knew the value of the ground-state energy (E_1) it would then be fairly easy to associate definite numerical values with all of the other energy levels, all the way up to E_∞ which would be equal to $E_1 + 13.60$ eV.

Now, we don't really know the value of E_1, but it makes life simpler for everyone if we all agree, as a matter of convention, that $E_\infty = 0$ eV. This corresponds to the energy of a separated electron and proton. It then follows that the ground-state energy is 13.60 eV below this, namely $E_1 = -13.60$ eV. Furthermore, each of the energy levels corresponding to excited states can then be associated with some *negative* value of energy between -13.60 eV and 0 eV. This is the convention that we will adopt for the rest of this block and it is also the convention that has been used to provide the energy values given on the right-hand side of Figure 2.11.

○ The emission lines in the visible part of the hydrogen spectrum all correspond to transitions down to the E_2 energy level. From which higher energy levels must a hydrogen atom make a transition in order to produce photons of energy 1.89 eV, 2.55 eV, 2.86 eV, 3.02 eV and 3.12 eV?

○ To produce photons of energy 1.89 eV a hydrogen atom must make a transition from E_3 to E_2 since

$$E_3 - E_2 = (-1.51 \text{ eV}) - (-3.40 \text{ eV}) = 1.89 \text{ eV}$$

Similarly

$$E_4 - E_2 = (-0.85 \text{ eV}) - (-3.40 \text{ eV}) = 2.55 \text{ eV}$$
$$E_5 - E_2 = (-0.54 \text{ eV}) - (-3.40 \text{ eV}) = 2.86 \text{ eV}$$
$$E_6 - E_2 = (-0.38 \text{ eV}) - (-3.40 \text{ eV}) = 3.02 \text{ eV}$$
$$E_7 - E_2 = (-0.28 \text{ eV}) - (-3.40 \text{ eV}) = 3.12 \text{ eV}$$

(If you need help with subtracting negative numbers refer to the 'Handling negative numbers' software on the Block 1 CD-ROM or *SGSG* Maths Help Section 2.)

One final point about Figure 2.11. If you carefully examine the energies on the right-hand side, you will find that the energies of the various levels can be written as follows:

$$E_1 = -13.60\,\text{eV} = \frac{-13.60\,\text{eV}}{1}$$

$$E_2 = -3.40\,\text{eV} = \frac{-13.60\,\text{eV}}{4}$$

$$E_3 = -1.51\,\text{eV} = \frac{-13.60\,\text{eV}}{9}$$

$$E_4 = -0.85\,\text{eV} = \frac{-13.60\,\text{eV}}{16}$$

and so on.

○ Can you see a pattern in the numbers on the bottom of this series of fractions?

○ The number on the bottom is the square of the number that labels the energy level.

The energy E_n associated with the nth energy level is given by:

$$E_n = \frac{-13.60\,\text{eV}}{n^2} \qquad \text{(where } n = 1, 2, 3, \text{ etc.)} \tag{2.2}$$

This remarkably simple formula provides a wonderfully compact way of remembering everything that is shown in Figure 2.11. The formula applies only to the hydrogen atom; indeed, it is not possible to summarize all the energy levels of any other atom in a simple formula. Here is another pay-off for studying the simplest atom first.

Given the full range of energy levels represented in Figure 2.11, it is possible to identify *all* possible transitions between energy levels in the hydrogen atom and hence all the possible spectral lines. In the case of the hydrogen atom these transitions are grouped into named series, some of which are shown in Figure 2.12.

Question 2.9 (a) Does the formula for E_n agree with the values for E_1 and E_∞ shown in Figure 2.11?

(b) What does the formula predict for the energy levels associated with $n = 10$ and $n = 100$?

(c) According to the formula, what would be the energy of the photon associated with a transition from the $n = 10$ level to the $n = 11$ level? Would that photon be absorbed or emitted? ◀

Question 2.10 In which series of lines in the hydrogen spectrum do some of the lines lie in the visible part of the electromagnetic spectrum? ◀

Question 2.11 (a) Use Figure 2.11 to calculate the energies of the first five lines in the Lyman series, in order of increasing energy.

(b) What is the energy of the photons corresponding to the highest energy spectral line in the Lyman series?

(c) In which region of the electromagnetic spectrum would all these lines occur?

(d) What would this part of the spectrum look like if all the lines of the Lyman series were of equal brightness and you had the means to record them? Present your answer as a black and white sketch, and label the energies of the lines in electronvolts. ◀

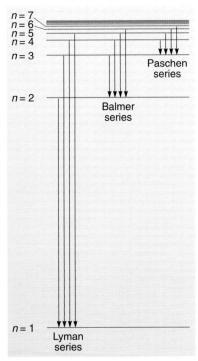

Figure 2.12 Some of the named series of transitions in the hydrogen atom that account for observed spectral lines. All spectral lines that arise from transitions having the ground-state energy E_1 as their lowest level are said to belong to the Lyman series. Those with the $n = 2$ level as their lowest level are said to belong to the Balmer series, and those with lowest level $n = 3$ belong to the Paschen series. (These series are named after the scientists who discovered them.)

2.7 Energy levels in general

So far we have been concentrating on the energies of atoms and you have seen that all atoms have energy levels. This is the remarkable feature that is new and different about quantum physics. In the type of physics you met in Block 5, there was nothing to prevent an object from having *any* amount of kinetic energy, or gravitational energy, or electrical energy, or any other kind of energy. The energy of everyday objects, such as cars, people, or locusts can vary continuously and take any value we care to choose. However, when we come down to the quantum world of atoms, things are very different.

2.7.1 Other quantum systems

It is now time to look beyond atoms, to apply these ideas to other aspects of the quantum world. Quantum physics, in fact, makes a bold and very general prediction: whenever particles are bound together, they form something that has energy levels. Atoms are a familiar example of this — because every atom consists of electrons bound together with a nucleus, the atom will have energy levels.

 Would you expect molecules to have energy levels? If so, what observable consequences would you expect?

Molecules are groups of atoms that are bound together, so you should expect that they will have energy levels. When molecules make transitions between their energy levels, they will emit or absorb photons which give rise to so-called molecular spectra.

Would you expect atomic nuclei to have energy levels? If so, what observable consequences would you expect?

Nuclei are groups of protons and neutrons that are bound together, so you should expect that they will have energy levels. When nuclei make transitions between their energy levels, they will emit or absorb photons which give rise to so-called nuclear spectra.

Experiments confirm these predictions of quantum physics: every day in laboratories all over the world, scientists study the spectra of molecules and nuclei. The idea of energy levels, so completely foreign to our experiences in the everyday world, is a routine part of the quantum world. In summary:

> Every system in which particles are bound together, such as nuclei, atoms or molecules will have *quantized* energy levels. Such systems are referred to as **quantum systems**.

Suppose you ionized a hydrogen atom, so that you freed its single electron from the atomic nucleus. Would you expect the separate electron and proton to be characterized by energy levels?

No — since the electron and proton are not bound together they do not have energy levels.

(a)

(b)

Figure 2.13 (a) The white-ish glow of an electric light bulb and (b) the red glow of a plate on an electric cooker. Both of these household appliances emit light that has a continuous spectrum. The glowing part of a plate or of a filament lamp is composed of metal and the light coming from such objects is emitted by the metal as a whole, rather than from individual atoms.

2.7.2 Continuous spectra

After this discussion of the line spectra of atoms, you may be wondering how it is possible to get a continuous spectrum, such as that shown earlier in Figure 2.2a. Continuous spectra contain a continuous distribution of photon energies. They can be produced by heating the tungsten filament of an electric light bulb to a very high temperature (Figure 2.13a), or by heating a plate on an electric cooker to a somewhat lower temperature (Figure 2.13b). The red glow from the hot-plate is not attributable to any particular photon energy; this spectrum is continuous, like that of the light bulb, except that the brightest part of the hot-plate's visible spectrum is the red part. Both these devices also emit radiation in other parts of the electromagnetic spectrum, such as infrared radiation.

The continuity of the spectrum from a heated object results from the fact that we are not studying emission from individual atoms, but the effect of many atoms together in a solid. In a solid metal, like tungsten, the atoms are arranged in a regular fashion, and some of the electrons are shared by the whole array of atoms. This is what makes the conduction of electricity possible. Though highly mobile, these electrons are confined, or bound, within the metal, so they are associated with energy levels. However, there are so many levels, and their energies are so close together, that they form a continuous energy band that is typically a few electronvolts wide. Transitions within this band give rise to a continuous range of photon energies, and hence a continuous spectrum. The energy levels of a metal therefore provide yet another example of quantized energy, in addition to the molecular, atomic and nuclear energy levels discussed above.

Question 2.12 Describe the general features that would be seen in the spectra produced by (a) a copper wire that is heated until it glows; (b) a vapour of copper atoms when an electric current is passed through it. (*Hint*: Think about the spectra produced by a tungsten light bulb filament, and by a vapour of sodium atoms, respectively.) ◄

2.8 Summary of Section 2

A photon is a particle of electromagnetic radiation. Monochromatic light, which has a single colour, consists of identical photons that each have exactly the same energy. The amount of energy carried by a single photon is called a quantum. Quanta of visible radiation (light) have energies of around 2 to 3 eV.

Each type of atom can be characterized by the energies of the photons it can absorb or emit. When these photons are dispersed to form a spectrum, the spectral lines of atomic spectra provide a unique 'spectral fingerprint' of the atoms concerned.

The explanation for atomic spectra is that atoms can only have certain values of energy, known as energy levels. Transitions, often referred to as quantum jumps, can occur between these energy levels. When an atom has its lowest possible energy, it is said to be in its ground state. To make atoms jump to excited states, which have a higher energy, photons of the correct energies must be supplied. When an atom jumps from one energy level to another of lower energy, the energy that it loses is taken away by a photon. The energy of the photon is equal to the *change* in energy of the atom:

$$E_{ph} = \Delta E_{atom} \tag{2.1}$$

Hydrogen has a relatively simple energy-level diagram, and various series of transitions can be identified from this. The energy E_n associated with the nth energy level of hydrogen is given by:

$$E_n = \frac{-13.60\,\text{eV}}{n^2} \tag{2.2}$$

Consequently, the energy of the ground state ($n = 1$) is $-13.60\,\text{eV}$.

Any system of particles that are bound together will have quantized energy levels. Free particles do not have energy levels.

Continuous spectra can be produced by heating solids, which have many energy levels with extremely small separations between them. These levels form a continuous energy band within which transitions are possible.

Activity 2.1   *Reflections on quantum ideas*

In Section 2 you have been introduced to one of the surprising revelations of quantum physics: atoms can only exist with certain values of energy. This activity allows you to reflect on the idea of quantized energy levels, and also on the fact that light is made up of photons. ◀

Quantum indeterminacy

One of the great attractions of Newton's laws that you met in Block 3 is that they deal in certainties. By using his laws of motion and gravity, everything from the motion of a pendulum to the motion of the planets can be predicted with a complete and reassuring certainty. As the French mathematician Pierre Simon de Laplace (1749–1827) famously pointed out, if you knew the positions and velocities of every atom everywhere, then Newton's laws would allow you to deduce both the entire history and the future of the Universe.

Yet scientists now know that it is simply not true that if you know the present state of something, you can necessarily predict its future with certainty. Never mind the entire Universe, it is not even possible to predict every aspect of the future of a single hydrogen atom.

The theory that dealt the mortal blow to Laplace's idea was quantum physics. You saw in the previous section how Planck's ideas shed light on atomic energies by showing that these energies have only certain, allowed values known as energy levels. But *why* do atoms have energy levels? This question could not be answered using the laws of physics that were known at the beginning of the 20th century. It became clear to a few young and exceptionally gifted scientists that a new approach was needed to describe the behaviour of atoms.

So, in the mid-1920s, quantum physics was born. This revolutionary theory actually enabled an understanding of atomic energy levels and a host of other atomic phenomena. One of the most important aspects of this new theory was its treatment of the behaviour of particles: quantum physics deals in *probabilities*. For example, whereas Newton's laws allow us to predict the exact path of an electron orbiting a nucleus, in fact electrons *do not* follow precisely defined paths and quantum physics provides a more accurate description of their motion.

In quantum physics we have to come to terms with intrinsic 'uncertainties' or, more accurately, *indeterminacies*. As you will see in this section, quantum physics says there are some things about atoms that are indeterminate, that is they cannot be known or determined, no matter how clever you are or how much computer power you have to hand. For instance, it is impossible to say exactly *where* an electron in an atom is at a certain time: the position is indeterminate.

Most people find it difficult to come to terms with the idea of quantum indeterminacy: Albert Einstein was the most famous conscientious objector to the very idea. 'God does not play dice', he famously remarked. He believed that it must be possible, if you have a good enough theory and good enough equipment, to probe, say, an atom in as much detail as you like. But, despite his brilliant arguments, nearly all quantum scientists believe that on this issue he was wrong.

So be prepared to spend time getting to grips with **indeterminacy**, one of the most challenging concepts in quantum physics. As a preparation, first read through Box 3.1, *What is probability?*

Box 3.1 What is probability?

Probability is a way of providing a quantitative measure of the 'chance' or 'likelihood' of a given event under given circumstances. For instance, suppose you have a 'fair' coin that can always be relied upon to have an equal likelihood of coming down heads or tails when given a fair toss. Then you could say that, as a result of a fair toss, the probability of obtaining heads is $\frac{1}{2}$ or 0.5 and the probability of obtaining tails is $\frac{1}{2}$ or 0.5. The fact that these two probabilities are equal indicates the 'fairness' of the coin, and the fact that they are both equal to 0.5 ensures that the total probability of obtaining either a head or a tail as the result of a fair toss is 1. It is a convention that a probability of 1 represents a certainty. In other words, by assigning probabilities of 0.5 to both heads *and* tails we are saying that there are only two possible outcomes, and they are equally likely.

- When rolling a fair dice (or die, as one is more properly called) there are six equally likely outcomes (1, 2, 3, 4, 5 or 6). What is the probability of any one of those outcomes?

- The probability of any one of the six outcomes is $\frac{1}{6}$.

In a great many identical repetitions of a given measurement, the probability of any particular outcome is equal to the *fraction* of the results which produced that particular outcome. In the case of the fair coin, if it were tossed four times the outcome might well be four heads or four tails, but if it were tossed four *million* times the outcome would almost certainly be very close to two million heads and two million tails. If the coin were tossed four *billion* times the fractions of heads and tails could be reasonably expected to be even closer to the 0.5s that represent the probabilities of the possible outcomes.

- If you rolled a die six million times, how many times would you expect the die to indicate a six?

- The probability of getting a six is $\frac{1}{6}$ so you would expect the die to indicate a six on about one million of the six million throws.

3.1 Indeterminacy and probability

When dealing with transitions between energy levels that require an increase in the energy of an atom, it is possible to exert some degree of control over which transitions occur by regulating the energies of the photons that are supplied to the atom. For example, suppose that a hydrogen atom is initially in its ground state, with energy E_1 on the energy-level diagram (the left-hand panel of Figure 3.1). You can

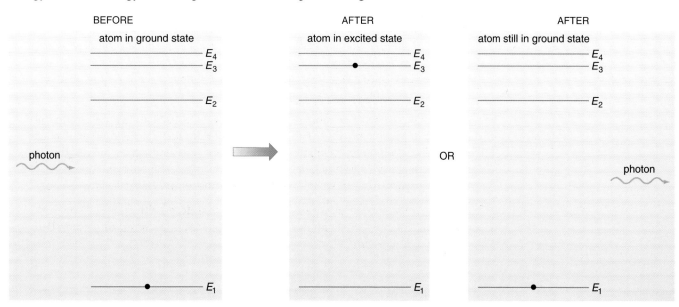

Figure 3.1 A photon with energy $E_3 - E_1$ may be absorbed by an atom in its ground state and excite the atom from energy level E_1 to energy level E_3, or it may just pass by leaving the atom unchanged. In quantum physics, it is not always the case that a photon which *can* be absorbed by an atom *will* actually be absorbed. Usually the best that can be done is to predict the probability of absorption.

ensure that the only upward transition this atom makes is to an energy E_3 by only providing the atom with photons of energy $E_3 - E_1$. These photons carry just the right amount of energy to cause the desired transition, but too little to cause the jump to E_4, and too much to cause the jump to E_2. Even so, quantum physics allows the atom a certain unpredictability in that although the atom *may* absorb a photon that has energy $E_3 - E_1$ it is not *required* to do so (the centre and right-hand panels of Figure 3.1). In a large number of identical encounters between hydrogen atoms and photons with this energy, all that can be predicted is the probability (i.e. the chance or relative likelihood) that the photons will be absorbed.

The significance of probability in quantum physics is even more apparent if you consider downward, rather than upward, transitions. Once again consider a hydrogen atom, this time initially in the E_3 energy level (see Figure 3.2). Such an atom may spontaneously make a downward transition, giving out a photon in the process. If it does so, that transition may involve the relatively small jump down to the E_2 level and the emission of a 1.89 eV photon of red light, or it might involve the much bigger jump down from the E_3 level to the E_1 level and the emission of a 12.09 eV photon.

⬤ In which part of the spectrum would you observe an emission line caused by 12.09 eV photons?

○ The ultraviolet. The energy is much greater than that of the 3.12 eV photons of the violet line in hydrogen's visible spectrum (see Figure 2.8).

Which transition will any particular hydrogen atom make? The answer is that no one knows and, more significantly, according to quantum physics, *no one can know*. Given a large number of identical hydrogen atoms all in the same energy level, all with energy E_3 say, it is possible to predict the proportion of them that will emit ultraviolet photons and jump to E_1, and the corresponding proportion that will emit visible photons and jump to E_2, but it is quite *impossible* to predict which of the two possible jumps will be made by any particular atom. We can summarize this idea in the following way.

> In quantum physics, the possible outcomes of a measurement can generally be predicted, and so can the probabilities (i.e. the relative likelihood) of each of those possible outcomes. However, it is not generally possible to predict definitely the outcome of any individual measurement if there is more than one possible outcome.

It is worth noting that there's a big difference between using probability to describe the outcome of tossing a coin and using it to describe photon emission. For instance, when tossing a coin it should be possible to predict the exact outcome of a given toss. Doing so is usually impracticable, since it involves knowing exactly how the coin was tossed, at what angle and at what speed, and with how much force and so on. It would certainly be very difficult to obtain all this information with the required precision, and it would be even harder to perform the required calculations, but there is no doubt that the outcome of the toss is fully determined by the laws of nature and could, in principle, be predicted.

The role of probability in quantum physics is really rather different from this. In quantum physics it is believed that even the most completely detailed description of a quantum system, such as an atom with a particular value of energy, will still only

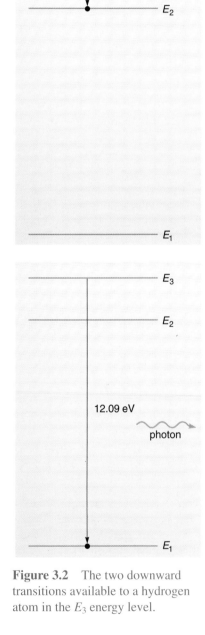

Figure 3.2 The two downward transitions available to a hydrogen atom in the E_3 energy level.

allow predictions to be made about the probabilities of different outcomes for the future behaviour of the system. In other words, in quantum physics, the use of probability is an *essential* feature and not simply a matter of convenience or practicality.

> The essential use of probability in quantum physics is another of its defining characteristics.

Quantum physics, with the built-in imprecision of a description of nature based on probabilities, is supported by experiment. Not a single experiment has ever disproved quantum physics.

Question 3.1   Which, if any, of the following statements are correct?

(a) When a hydrogen atom in its ground state is isolated from other sources of energy, it has no possibility of change.

(b) Intense radiation, with photons of energies ranging up to 10 eV, has absolutely no effect on hydrogen atoms in their ground state.

(c) If a hydrogen atom in its ground state absorbs a photon of energy 12.75 eV, there is no way of saying whether it will subsequently emit a visible photon. ◄

You can see that in quantum physics there is a distinctive combination of strong prohibition and unpredictable freedom. Despite the remarkable prohibitions in items (a) and (b) of Question 3.1, the quantum world seems to allow great licence: whatever is not actually forbidden will be found to occur, sometime or other. Nonetheless, the fact that even the most detailed description of a quantum system still involves probability shows that indeterminacy is at the heart of quantum physics.

Having learned the importance of indeterminacy, you are now in a position to appreciate the problems of formulating a detailed account of the inner workings of the atom. In the next three sections (Sections 3.2 to 3.4) we shall examine three attempts to formulate such an account, the first two of which failed precisely because they were concocted before the significance of quantum indeterminacy was properly appreciated.

3.2   The Rutherford model of the atom

In Block 6 you were introduced to what is usually known as the Rutherford model of the atom (see Figure 3.3). This was based on the view that an atom consists of a tiny dense nucleus being orbited by one or more electrons, in much the same way that planets orbit the Sun. Unlike the Solar System, in which the planets are held in their orbits by their gravitational attraction to the Sun, Rutherford's atom was held together by the electrical attraction between the positively charged nucleus and the negatively charged electrons. Nonetheless, the similarities between the Rutherford model of the atom and the Solar System run deep: just as an isolated planet following a given orbit has a fixed amount of energy determined by its speed and distance from the Sun, so an orbiting electron has a fixed amount of energy determined by its speed and distance from the nucleus. As noted in Section 2.4, the speed determines the kinetic energy of the electron, and the distance from the nucleus determines its electrical energy. The energy of the atom is just the sum of these contributions. Smaller orbits (closer to the nucleus) have a lower electrical energy and correspond to a lower energy for the atom. Such close orbits indicate that the electron is tightly bound to the nucleus, requiring a large amount of energy to remove the electron.

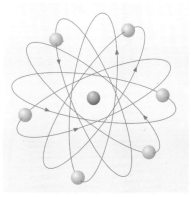

Figure 3.3   The internal structure of an atom according to the Rutherford model (*c.* 1911). In this model, electrons orbit the positively charged nucleus. The example shown here, with six electrons, corresponds to the carbon atom.

The Rutherford model is still useful for some purposes, but it is badly flawed and quite incapable of accounting for the inner workings of the atom. The most important of its failings is that it provides no explanation for the existence of spectral lines. Even though particular electron orbits might be associated with particular energy levels of the atom, there is nothing in the Rutherford model that prevents the electron from absorbing arbitrary amounts of energy and moving into an orbit that does not correspond to an allowed energy level. Thus the absorption spectrum of a Rutherford atom might be expected to be a continuous spectrum rather that a line spectrum. Clearly, the Rutherford model is incomplete and there is a need for a more credible model of the atom.

3.3 The Bohr model of the atom

One of Rutherford's students, the Danish physicist Niels Bohr (Figure 3.4), is credited with formulating the first 'quantum' model of the atom. His masterstroke was to graft quantum ideas on to Rutherford's basic atomic model. The result, the **Bohr model of the atom**, was really a sort of 'half-way house' between the Rutherford model of 1911 and the fully quantum models that were formulated in the 1920s.

The Bohr model of the hydrogen atom is based on the assumption that each energy level of the hydrogen atom corresponds to a particular circular orbit of the electron around the nucleus (Figure 3.5). Although Bohr used Newton's laws to describe the motion of the electron, he assumed — somewhat arbitrarily — that only certain orbits are possible.

Figure 3.4 Niels Bohr (1885–1962). As physicist and philosopher, he had a profound influence upon the development of quantum physics; as a goalkeeper, he narrowly missed selection for the Danish football team in the 1908 Olympic games. By all accounts, Bohr revelled in the difficulties of interpreting quantum physics and of reconciling the predictions of the theory with what is generally known as common sense. 'You never understand quantum physics, you just get used to it', he once remarked, no doubt with some satisfaction.

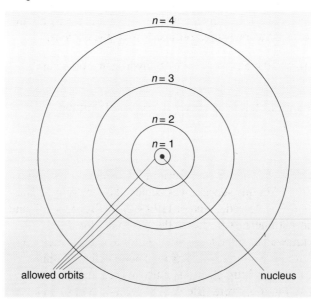

Figure 3.5 In the Bohr model of the hydrogen atom, each orbit is characterized by a whole number n and corresponds to a particular energy level. The energies of the allowed orbits correspond to the energy levels of the hydrogen atom.

The result of Bohr's calculations was that the allowed orbits could each be characterized by a whole number n, a particular orbital radius r_n and by a particular value of energy E_n. These energies then correspond to the energy levels of the atom when the electron occupies the orbits concerned. The model predicted that the energy levels of a hydrogen atom are given by:

$$E_n = \frac{-13.60\,\text{eV}}{n^2} \qquad \text{(where } n = 1, 2, 3, 4, \text{etc.)} \qquad (3.1)$$

This result was a triumph for the Bohr model: the energy levels predicted were exactly the same as those that had been obtained experimentally by measuring the energies of photons emitted and absorbed by hydrogen atoms (Equation 2.2).

Bohr also predicted that the radii r_n of the allowed orbits of the electron in a hydrogen atom are given by:

$$r_n = n^2 \times 5.29 \times 10^{-11}\,\text{m} \tag{3.2}$$

So a large value of n implies that the electron will orbit at a large radius from the nucleus. A large radius implies a large electrical energy, and therefore a large energy for the atom. Therefore the higher energy levels simply correspond to electron orbits further from the nucleus. (Don't forget that the larger the value of n in Equation 3.1, the smaller the negative number and therefore the higher the energy.)

Bohr also calculated the speed of the electron when it occupies each of the allowed orbits. Furthermore, Bohr assumed that the atom could absorb or emit radiation only when the electron made the transition from one allowed orbit to another (Figure 3.6). When such transitions occurred the energy lost or gained by the atom could be carried away (or supplied) by a single photon, in accord with Planck's quantum hypothesis. In other words, Bohr required the electron in his atom to make 'quantum jumps' between the allowed orbits.

Bohr's model may have been an odd mixture of quantum physics and Newton's laws, but no one could doubt its success in accounting for the spectral fingerprint of the hydrogen atom. Moreover, the model also allowed an interpretation of the mysterious whole number n that characterized hydrogen's energy levels: this number simply characterizes the orbit of the electron. For example, when the atom has energy E_2, the electron is in the second allowed orbit as measured outwards from the nucleus.

⬤ What is the radius of the orbit of the electron when the hydrogen atom is in its ground state?

◯ When the atom is in its ground state, it is characterized by $n = 1$. Putting this value into Equation 3.2, we find:

$$r_1 = 5.29 \times 10^{-11}\,\text{m}$$

So Bohr's theory, unlike Rutherford's, had the great merit of being able to account for the spectrum of the hydrogen atom. Yet this success was achieved by making *ad hoc* assumptions about which orbits were allowed. A major failing of the Bohr model, and of the Rutherford model too for that matter, was due to the fact that it involved *orbiting* electrons. It had been known since the late 19th century that an accelerating electric charge, such as an electron, is a source of electromagnetic radiation (this is how radio waves are generated). The orbiting electrons must be continuously accelerating, since they are travelling in a circle (Block 3, Section 4), and so they should *continuously* emit radiation, which would in turn carry energy away from the atom. This continuous emission of energy would cause the electrons to spiral in to the nucleus in a tiny fraction of a second. Such a rapid collapse of the atom is totally inconsistent with the manifest stability of ordinary matter. Clearly then, the Bohr model, with its stable fixed orbits, is inconsistent with the real world.

The key point to remember though is that the Bohr model showed that quantum physics had an essential role to play in explaining the internal workings of the atom. In this way, the model paved the way for the development of a fully 'quantum' model of the atom.

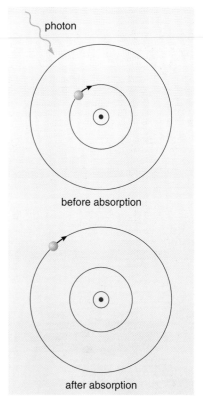

photon

before absorption

after absorption

Figure 3.6 In the Bohr model, transitions between energy levels occur when electrons make quantum jumps between allowed orbits. These jumps are accompanied by the emission or absorption of radiation, in accord with Planck's quantum idea. In the example shown here, a photon is absorbed by an atom, causing the electron to jump from the second to the third orbit.

Question 3.2 According to the Bohr model, what happens when a hydrogen atom makes a transition between the energy level E_3 and the ground state? Specify, in as much detail as you can, what the electron does, what the radii and energies of the two orbits involved are, and whether a photon is emitted or absorbed. ◀

Question 3.3 Describe in words (with no equations) what happens according to the Bohr model when hydrogen atoms emit the spectral lines in the Balmer series (see Figure 2.12). ◀

3.4 The Schrödinger model of the atom

The Rutherford and Bohr models of the atom both encapsulate crucial stages in the development of ideas about the structure of the atom, but — as you've seen — they are deeply flawed. Both fall a long way short of representing the reality of the quantum world as we currently understand it. The richly detailed understanding of chemistry and the physics of atoms that modern science provides is firmly rooted in a different model of the atom — a model that fully incorporates the essential indeterminacy of quantum physics. It is to this fundamentally important model of the atom that we now turn.

The quantum model of the atom that is used today emerged from the work of a number of European physicists in the mid-1920s. One of the most influential members of this group was the Austrian theoretical physicist Erwin Schrödinger (Figure 3.7), who proposed an equation that did for quantum physics what Newton's second law did for the theory of motion. The quantum model of the atom is most easily studied in terms of the Schrödinger equation, so it is convenient to refer to the model as the **Schrödinger model of the atom**, despite a certain degree of historical injustice.

The model is mathematically complex but, don't worry, we shall be concentrating on its basic concepts and results rather than the methods used to obtain them. As usual we shall concentrate on the hydrogen atom, but it's worth noting that the model can successfully describe all other atoms too.

When the Schrödinger equation is applied to the hydrogen atom, it predicts:

1 that the atom has energy levels $E_n = \dfrac{-13.60\,\text{eV}}{n^2}$;

2 detailed information about the speed and location of the electron when the atom has an energy corresponding to each of those energy levels.

The first of these points confirms that the Schrödinger equation accounts for the emission and absorption spectra (the 'spectral fingerprint') of hydrogen. It is the second point that separates it from Bohr's 'half-way house' in that the Schrödinger equation predicts that the behaviour of the electron in the atom is intrinsically indeterminate.

3.4.1 The Schrödinger model for the ground state of the hydrogen atom

According to quantum physics, if a hydrogen atom has a certain amount of energy, it is impossible to say in advance of a measurement what value will be obtained for the electron's position or speed. This means that if identical measurements are made on atoms with the same energy, these experiments will give a variety of different outcomes. What *can* be predicted, as far as position and speed are concerned, are all the possible outcomes of a measurement and the probabilities of each of those outcomes.

Figure 3.7 In 1925, when he was enjoying an illicit weekend with one of his partners, Erwin Schrödinger (1887–1961) formulated an equation that may be thought of as the quantum counterpart of Newton's laws of motion. The equation allows one, in principle, to find the energy levels of any atom. In practice, only the solutions for the hydrogen atom are easy to obtain. (The letter 'ö' in Schrödinger's name is pronounced like the 'er' of 'her'.)

To begin with we concentrate on the electron's position. Because of the uncertainty in the outcome of any experiment to find the position of an electron in a hydrogen atom, we need a new way of illustrating the atom. (The same goes, by the way, for all other atoms.) We can't show the electron as having a definite orbit; somehow, we have to incorporate some uncertainty into our visualization. A good way of illustrating the electron is to depict it in terms of an **electron probability cloud** or an *electron cloud* for short. In Figure 3.8, the electron cloud is illustrated for the case in which the hydrogen atom is in its ground state.

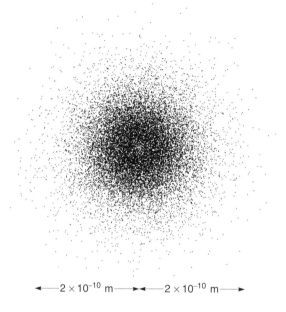

Figure 3.8 An electron probability cloud visualization of the electron in a hydrogen atom in its ground state. The cloud is three dimensional, and here we have represented a slice through its centre. The nucleus, at the centre, is too small to see on this scale.

$\longleftarrow 2 \times 10^{-10}$ m $\longrightarrow \longleftarrow 2 \times 10^{-10}$ m $\longrightarrow$

The cloud is dense in those regions where there is a high probability of finding the ground-state electron, and thin in those regions where the electron is unlikely to be found. It is important to remember that the electron cloud is not in any sense a 'picture' of the electron. It's not the electron itself that is spread out around the nucleus, but the *probability of finding* the electron. One way of thinking about such a cloud is as follows.

Imagine that you could perform an experiment to measure the position of the electron within a hydrogen atom. If you did this ten thousand times, and each time drew a dot at the location where you found the electron to be, the result would be something like Figure 3.8. Of course Figure 3.8 is only a two-dimensional drawing of the real three-dimensional situation, but it gives the general idea.

Quantum physics does not allow us to predict the outcome of any individual measurement of the electron's distance from the nucleus, but the Schrödinger model does allow us to be quite precise, in a probabilistic sense. For example, suppose we want to know the probability that a measurement of the electron's distance from the nucleus will yield a value between 2.4×10^{-11} m and 2.6×10^{-11} m. Well, the Schrödinger equation predicts that for every 10 000 measurements on hydrogen atoms in their ground states, 131 of them should yield positions for the electron that are within this particular range. If we were to repeat this calculation for a variety of other small ranges of distance then we could build up a histogram

Figure 3.9 A histogram showing the predicted results of 10 000 measurements of the position of the electron in a hydrogen atom in its ground state, in terms of its distance from the nucleus (i.e. the proton). The horizontal axis shown here ends at $r = 20 \times 10^{-11}$ m, but there is a small probability of detecting the electron at even larger radii.

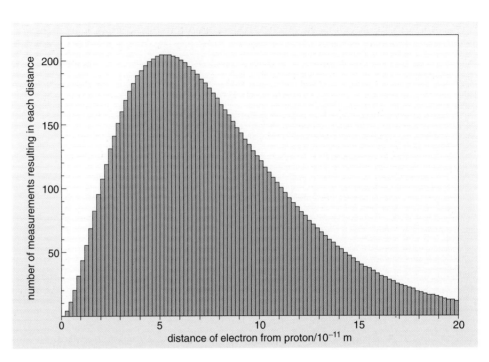

to show the predicted results of all of these 10 000 measurements, such as that shown in Figure 3.9. Each column of the histogram spans a range of 0.2×10^{-11} m.

The electron may clearly be found at any one of a whole range of distances from the nucleus, but the most likely distance at which the electron will be found is indicated by the peak in the histogram. When determined accurately, the most probable distance turns out to be $r = 5.29 \times 10^{-11}$ m, which is *exactly* the radius predicted by the Bohr model for the electron's orbit when the hydrogen atom is in its ground state. So, although Schrödinger's model is very different from Bohr's and does not involve orbits, it does suggest why Bohr's orbit-based model was able to provide some insights into the behaviour of hydrogen. Broadly speaking, the orbits in the Bohr model are located at the radii at which the electron is most likely to be detected, according to the Schrödinger model.

⬤ Using Figure 3.9, how many of the 10 000 measurements for the position of the electron will be between 5.2×10^{-11} m and 5.4×10^{-11} m, i.e. roughly at the most probable distance from the proton?

◯ Figure 3.9 shows that the column centred at about 5.3×10^{-11} m from the proton contains 205 of the 10 000 measurements.

The 205 measurements that are within 0.1×10^{-11} m of the most probable radius will be distributed in a thin 'spherical shell' around the nucleus at a distance of 5.3×10^{-11} m from it. So in Figure 3.8, these measurements are spread over a relatively large volume of space. In contrast, the 11 measurements centred on a radius of 0.5×10^{-11} m, for instance, are distributed around a much smaller spherical shell (because it is closer to the nucleus). For this reason, the electron cloud in Figure 3.8 appears *most* dense at small radii, and *not* at a radius of 5.29×10^{-11} m as one might at first expect.

Similar conclusions apply to the speed of the electron moving around the nucleus. If thousands of measurements were made of the electron's speed in the ground-state hydrogen atom, a range of possible outcomes would be found. There is a most probable speed, which again corresponds to the speed predicted by the Bohr model, but the range of speeds would follow a distribution similar to that shown in Figure 3.9 for the electron's position.

As you can see, the Schrödinger model manages to be precise without being prescriptive in individual cases: its predictions are an extraordinary blend of definiteness and indeterminacy.

Question 3.4 What is the difference between the predictions of the Schrödinger model and the Bohr model concerning the position of the electron in a hydrogen atom that is in its ground state? Word your answer as precisely as you can. ◀

For an electron in a hydrogen atom in its ground state, the Schrödinger equation makes a clear prediction for the electron probability cloud. As you will see shortly, the equation makes very different predictions for the electron probability cloud when the atom is in an excited state.

3.4.2 The Schrödinger model and the excited states of the hydrogen atom

So far we have discussed the Schrödinger model's predictions for the hydrogen atom only when it has the lowest possible energy, $E_1 = -13.60\,\text{eV}$. However, the model gives a comprehensive description of the atom when it has an energy corresponding to each of the other energy levels too.

Figure 3.10 shows the electron probability clouds corresponding to the ground state and some of the excited states of the hydrogen atom. The important point to notice is that, for the E_2 and E_3 energy levels, there are several different electron probability clouds, each of which corresponds to the *same* energy level. Now, we have said that when the hydrogen atom has its lowest energy then it is in its ground state, and when it has a higher energy then it is in an excited state. A general name for these states of the atom is **quantum states** (or just *states* for short) and each quantum state has a precisely defined amount of energy — one of the energy levels of the atom. According to the Schrödinger model though, there is *more than one* quantum state corresponding to each energy level of the hydrogen atom.

If a number of quantum states have the same energy, in just what way are they different? Part of the answer is that even if two quantum states correspond to the same energy level, they may still be characterized by different electron probability clouds. That this is the case is demonstrated in Figure 3.10. As you can see, the clouds in each row have a variety of forms, indicating measurable differences between the states, even though they have the same energy. Different quantum states also differ in other properties, that are not relevant to the current discussion.

One final piece of terminology: in the hydrogen atom, the *electron* can be said to *occupy* a particular quantum state of the atom. The reason for this is that it is only the possible values of the location and speed of the *electron* that vary from one quantum state to another — the nucleus of the atom is unchanged. So when a hydrogen atom undergoes a transition from one quantum state to another, the state that the electron

Figure 3.10 Electron probability clouds corresponding to *some* of the quantum states of the hydrogen atom. Note, whereas Figure 3.8 represented the possible locations of the electron by dots, here we use a grey-scale to represent the probability of finding the electron at any location. The darker the shade, the higher the probability of finding the electron at that location. The labels for the states (such as 1s, 2p) are explained in Section 3.4.3. Note the banding in the grey tones is an artefact of the printing process. In reality there is a continuous gradation of probability.

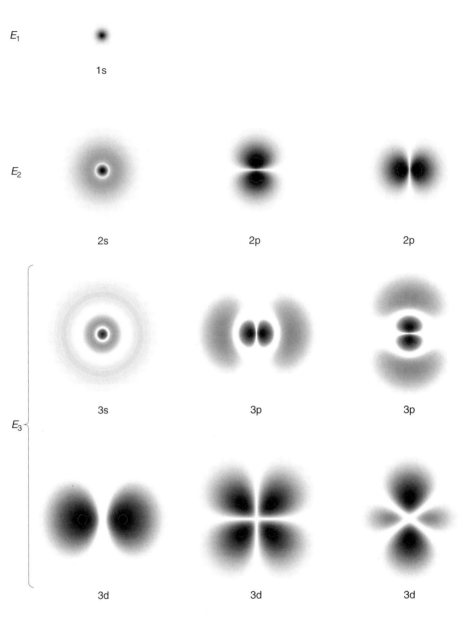

occupies after the transition will be different from that which it occupied before the transition. The crucial point is that energy levels and quantum states apply to atoms as a whole, but in the hydrogen atom we can say that the single electron *occupies* a particular quantum state.

Let's look at some examples. There are two quantum states corresponding to the energy level E_1, eight quantum states corresponding to the energy level E_2, 18 quantum states corresponding to the energy level E_3, and 32 quantum states corresponding to the energy level E_4. There is a pattern here.

According to the Schrödinger model of the hydrogen atom, there are $2n^2$ different quantum states that correspond to the nth energy level of hydrogen.

The two quantum states corresponding to the energy level E_1 have the same electron clouds (see Figure 3.10); and in general *pairs* of quantum states correspond to each of the electron clouds shown in the other rows of Figure 3.10.

⬤ How many different quantum states of hydrogen are associated with the energy levels corresponding to $n = 5$ and $n = 10$?

○ Using the expression $2n^2$ for the given values of n: corresponding to the fifth level there are $2 \times 5^2 = 50$ different states with energy E_5, and corresponding to the tenth level there are $2 \times 10^2 = 200$ different states with energy E_{10}.

3.4.3 Quantum numbers

The fact that there are different quantum states corresponding to a single energy level means that, to label a given state of a hydrogen atom, we need more than just the number n that sufficed to label the energy levels. Consequently, each of these different quantum states can be characterized by a unique set of **quantum numbers**. You can think of these numbers simply as labels that serve to distinguish between different states occupied by the electron in the hydrogen atom. (In fact, as you will see in Section 4, the same numbers can be used for an electron in *any* atom.)

When labelling quantum states, the number n is called the **principal quantum number** of the state and it can be any positive whole number: 1 or 2 or 3 or 4, etc. The principal quantum number n determines the energy of a given quantum state in the hydrogen atom, as shown by Equation 3.1. So, all states with a given value of n have the same energy in the hydrogen atom.

To specify a state completely, we need the values of some additional quantum numbers. The Schrödinger model generally requires three additional quantum numbers for this purpose, but the first of these additional quantum numbers is the most important. It is usually given the symbol l and, when used to distinguish states that share a common value of n, it is only allowed to take the whole-number values from 0 up to $n - 1$. So, the maximum value of l is one short of the value of n. For example, any state with $n = 1$ (the lowest allowed value of n) must have $l = 0$ (as $n - 1 = 0$), but among the eight different states with $n = 2$ there will be some with $l = 0$ and others with $l = 1$ (the maximum value of l as $n - 1 = 1$). Among the 18 states with $n = 3$ there will be some with $l = 0$, some with $l = 1$ and some with $l = 2$.

⬤ What are the possible values of l for states with $n = 5$?

○ Following the rule that l can take any value from 0 to $n - 1$, l could be 0, 1, 2, 3 or 4.

The two quantum numbers n and l still don't specify all the possible states corresponding to an energy level. Two more quantum numbers and further rules ensure that there are $2 \times (2l + 1)$ different states for each pair of allowed values of n and l. For example, the number of different states with $n = 4$ and $l = 3$ is $2 \times (2 \times 3 + 1) = 14$. Each quantum state has its own unique set of quantum numbers which specify it completely, i.e. each of the 14 states with $n = 4$ and $l = 3$ is distinguished from each other by the remaining quantum numbers. Fortunately, the details of these other two quantum numbers are not of great significance in the context of the present discussion, so we shall not pursue them. Instead let's simply investigate the significance of what has already been said.

⬤ How many different states are there with $n = 5$ and $l = 2$?

◯ $2 \times (2l + 1) = 2 \times (2 \times 2 + 1) = 10$.

The existence of $2n^2$ different quantum states corresponding to each value of n (and hence to each energy level) can now be fully accounted for in terms of the three rules that have been introduced so far.

> Rule 1   The principal quantum number n may be any positive whole number (1, 2, 3, etc.) and this number determines the energy level of the hydrogen atom.
>
> Rule 2   For a given value of n, the quantum number l may take any whole-number value from 0 up to $n - 1$.
>
> Rule 3   For given values of n and l there are $2 \times (2l + 1)$ different quantum states.

As an example, consider the states with energy E_2 that correspond to the next-to-lowest energy level of the hydrogen atom. All of these states will have $n = 2$ (Rule 1), so the only values of l they are allowed to have are 0 or 1 (Rule 2). How many of these states will there be in total? Well, using Rule 3, there are $2 \times (2 \times 0 + 1) = 2$ states with $l = 0$, and $2 \times (2 \times 1 + 1) = 6$ states with $l = 1$. The total number of possible states with energy E_2 is therefore $2 + 6 = 8$. This is exactly the number predicted by the $2n^2$ rule of the Schrödinger model you met earlier.

Question 3.5   Use the three rules above to demonstrate why there are 18 possible states with energy E_3. ◀

So much for the counting of states. Now for an important piece of notation. It is rather tedious to keep saying 'a state with $n = 2$ and $l = 0$', to distinguish it from 'a state with $n = 2$ and $l = 1$', so a different convention is commonly used among scientists. This involves identifying the value of l by means of a letter, with s for 0, p for 1, d for 2 and f for 3. Values of l from 4 onwards are then assigned the alphabetic sequence g, h, i, etc.

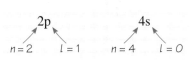

The convention is to show the values n and l that correspond to a particular state by writing the numerical value of n and the letter representing l next to each other. Thus, the ground state of hydrogen, with $n = 1$ and $l = 0$, is a 1s state; an excited state of hydrogen with $n = 2$ and $l = 1$ simply becomes a 2p state; and a 4s state would be an excited state for which $n = 4$ and $l = 0$.

The use of s, p, d, f to represent the numbers 0, 1, 2, 3 arose for historical reasons. The letters once stood for 'sharp', 'principal', 'diffuse' and 'fundamental', from terms used to describe lines in spectra. But this doesn't really help you to remember them, and the use of the convention is now so widespread that there is really no alternative but to commit it to memory. Here are some questions to help you to remember the sequence.

⬤ What are the values of n and l for the following states: (a) 3p; (b) 2s; (c) 4d?

◯ (a) For a 3p state, $n = 3$ and $l = 1$; (b) for a 2s state, $n = 2$ and $l = 0$; (c) for a 4d state, $n = 4$ and $l = 2$.

⬤ What is the conventional way to describe states with (a) $n = 5$ and $l = 3$; (b) $n = 3$ and $l = 2$; (c) $n = 1$ and $l = 0$?

◯ (a) 5f; (b) 3d; (c) 1s.

⬤ Which of the following are not possible states, because they break one of the rules on page 38: 1p, 2s, 2p, 3d, 3f?

◯ 1p is impossible since p stands for $l = 1$, which is not allowed for $n = 1$, and 3f is impossible since f stands for $l = 3$, which is not allowed for $n = 3$. The others are allowed states.

Question 3.6   (a) How many 4s, 4p, 4d and 4f states are there for a hydrogen atom?

(b) What are the energies of these states?

(c) Do these states account for all the excited states of hydrogen with that energy? ◀

3.4.4   Electron clouds for excited states of hydrogen

To end this discussion of the Schrödinger model and indeterminacy, it is appropriate to look a little more carefully at the electron probability clouds that correspond to some of the excited states of the hydrogen atom. Figures 3.11 and 3.12 show, respectively, enlarged versions of the 2s and 2p states that were shown in Figure 3.10. It is a striking fact that these two states have very different electron probability clouds, and this of course implies observable differences between the states.

Question 3.7   What is the significance of the white ring in Figure 3.11? ◀

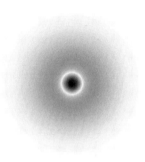

Figure 3.11   Electron cloud depiction of a 2s state of hydrogen.

Question 3.8   Does Figure 3.12 mean that the electron is in two places at the same time? If not, what do the two 'lobes' of the electron cloud signify? ◀

The nature of the 2s and 2p states of hydrogen really does make it plain that the quantum physical behaviour of atoms is very different from the sort of behaviour we might expect from our everyday experience of the world. In each case there is one electron, yet two separated regions where it is likely to be found. How can it be in two regions at the same time? Well, of course, it can't. It's not the electron that is split but the probability of finding the electron when its position is measured. The question of *how* the electron gets from one region to the other is not addressed by quantum physics.

Quantum physics certainly does not support a picture in which the electron is jumping back and forth in some way just waiting to be detected in one region or the other. Indeed, according to the conventional view of quantum physics, the electron does not have any particular position until its position is measured. It is the act of measurement that gives the electron a position, and even then the position is only likely to be known at the time of the measurement. As soon as you stop looking, your knowledge of where the electron is will rapidly become more and more imprecise.

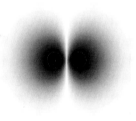

Figure 3.12   Electron cloud depiction of one of the 2p states of hydrogen.

Activity 3.1   Quantum states

This activity allows you to consolidate your understanding of quantum states and quantum numbers. ◀

3.5   The lessons of indeterminacy

You have seen that quantum states of a hydrogen atom exist that are characterized by a *definite* value of the energy, but by *indeterminate* values for the position and speed of the electron. However, the typical range of positions can be predicted for each quantum state (Figure 3.10) as can the typical range of speeds. The probabilities with which any particular position or speed will be measured can also be predicted.

Figure 3.13 Werner Karl Heisenberg (1901–1976) was a German theoretical physicist and, although his methods for understanding the quantum nature of atoms were somewhat different and more complex than those of Schrödinger, the two methods were later shown to be equivalent. Heisenberg was a great theoretician, but his practical skills left something to be desired. In his oral examination for a doctorate, his responses to questions on experimental physics were so poor that one of his distinguished examiners recommended that he should fail. He was, however, eventually awarded a pass for the exam — with the lowest possible grade.

In principle, at least, it is possible to devise experiments to measure the position of an electron in a hydrogen atom. It is also possible to devise experiments to measure the speed and direction of motion of the electron. (Recall from Block 3 that the scientific name referring to 'speed and direction of motion' is *velocity*.) But can *both* the position and velocity be measured simultaneously, so tying down the behaviour of the electron precisely? It turns out that the answer is no. A fundamental result of quantum physics, discovered in 1927 by Werner Heisenberg (Figure 3.13), explicitly rules out such detailed knowledge.

> The Heisenberg **uncertainty principle** rules out the possibility of combining definite knowledge of some quantities (such as position) with definite knowledge of certain other quantities (such as velocity). It also limits the accuracy with which such quantities can be measured simultaneously.

According to the uncertainty principle, measuring one quantity with a prescribed level of accuracy automatically limits the accuracy with which the other can be known at the time of the measurement. Indeed, the uncertainty principle says that if you know the exact position of a particle, you can know nothing at all about its velocity at the same time. The converse is also true: if you know its velocity exactly, you can't know anything about its position simultaneously.

To get some idea of why this is the case, think about what measuring the position of an electron might actually involve. The obvious way to measure the position is to 'see' where the electron is, and to 'see' where something is you have to shine light on it. But shining light on an atom will have one of two effects. On the one hand, a photon may be absorbed, so causing the atom to jump to another energy level, in which case the state of the atom has changed. Alternatively, the photons may not interact with the atom, but emerge unaffected, in which case you haven't measured anything! In other words, by measuring the position of the electron in an atom, you will change the energy of the atom, and so alter the possible range of velocities of the electron. Indeed, *any* act of measurement on a hydrogen atom, or any other quantum system, will involve transferring energy into or out of that system, and so will change the quantum state.

Question 3.9   Which one of the following statements is correct? Explain your answer in each case.

(a) The Heisenberg uncertainty principle says that everything about the motion of a particle is uncertain.

(b) The more accurately the velocity of a particle is known, the less accurately the value of its position can be known at the same time.

(c) Eventually, an experimenter is bound to build apparatus that will enable both the position and velocity of an atomic electron to be determined to arbitrarily high precision.

(d) When he formulated his uncertainty principle, Heisenberg was implicitly criticizing the skill of his experimental colleagues. ◄

It is important to appreciate that the limitations of the uncertainty principle are a matter of deep principle in quantum physics, not a result of sloppy work or poor equipment. The quantum world is not only essentially indeterminate, it is also inherently uncertain.

In the everyday world, however, we can largely forget about quantum indeterminacy and the Heisenberg uncertainty principle. The reason for this is that atoms, and other quantum systems, are so very small and have such a tiny mass. The more massive an object is, the less important are the effects of indeterminacy. For instance, the uncertainties in the position or velocity of a massive object, such as a planet orbiting the Sun, are so tiny that they are utterly insignificant and we can, in effect, measure the position and velocity of a planet as accurately as our measuring instruments allow. In general, quantum indeterminacy is only apparent when dealing with things on an atomic scale, or smaller.

3.6 Summary of Section 3

In quantum physics, the possible outcomes of a measurement can generally be predicted, and so can their probabilities. However, it is not generally possible to predict definitely the outcome of any individual measurement when there is more than one possible outcome.

The Bohr model of the hydrogen atom is based on the assumption that each energy level of the atom corresponds to a precisely defined circular orbit of the electron around the central nucleus. Only certain orbits are allowed.

The Schrödinger model of the atom embraces the indeterminacy of quantum physics and does away with orbits. In the case of the hydrogen atom, the model provides definite predictions for the energy levels, and probabilistic predictions concerning measurements of quantities such as the position or speed of the electron. One way to represent the location of an electron is by an electron probability cloud.

According to the Schrödinger model of the hydrogen atom there are $2n^2$ different quantum states corresponding to the nth energy level. Each state is uniquely identified by the values of a set of quantum numbers, the most important of which are denoted n and l. There are $2 \times (2l + 1)$ different states for each pair of allowed values of n and l, and l can take any whole-number value from 0 up to $n - 1$. States with l values of 0, 1, 2, 3 and 4 are described as s states, p states, d states, f states and g states, respectively. Different quantum states can be represented by different electron probability clouds.

The Heisenberg uncertainty principle states that one cannot simultaneously have precise knowledge of the position and velocity of an electron in an atom (or any other quantum system). It emphasizes the impossibility of avoiding indeterminacy in the quantum world.

Activity 2.1 *Reflections on quantum ideas (continued)*

In Section 3 you have been introduced to yet more surprising aspects of quantum physics. Now is the time to return to Activity 2.1 and to reflect further on these ideas. ◀

Activity 3.2 *Testing your strategies*

In Block 6 Activity 15.1 you thought about your strategies for dealing with difficult concepts. We ask you now to consider these strategies further. ◀

4 Atomic structure

Having examined some of the distinctive characteristics of quantum physics in the earlier parts of this block we are now ready to complete the process of 'taking the world apart'. That is the aim of this section and the two that follow. As you work through Sections 4, 5 and 6 you will see the ideas that have been developed earlier in the block being applied on smaller and smaller size scales (see Figure 1.5). The quantum systems being considered and the typical size scales involved are as follows:

Section 4: electrons in atoms, 10^{-10} m

Section 5: nucleons in nuclei, 10^{-14} m

Section 6: quarks in nucleons, from 10^{-15} m to the smallest size scales currently detectable (about 10^{-18} m)

In each of these sections we have provided you with a CD-ROM activity that allows you to investigate the behaviour of the relevant particles. You will see that investigating these successively smaller size scales requires the use of increasingly large amounts of energy. That's why there is a limit to the smallest size scales so far investigated. However, remarkable as it may seem, so far the evidence indicates that the principles of quantum physics, and the characteristic quantum phenomena of energy levels and indeterminacy, continue to provide a reliable guide to the nature of the physical world at even the smallest scales.

From Block 6, you already know the ingredients for a description of atomic structure. An atom of atomic number Z contains Z electrons, each of charge $-e$, which counterbalance the charge $+Ze$ of the Z protons in the atom's nucleus, making the whole atom electrically neutral. The charge of each proton has the value $e = 1.6 \times 10^{-19}$ C. The nucleus of an atom also contains $(A - Z)$ neutrons, where A is the mass number.

4.1 Atoms and ions with a single electron

Our aim in the rest of this section is to develop an understanding of the structure of atoms in general. We have already made a start on this, in Sections 2 and 3, by examining the hydrogen atom in particular. What we shall now do is to use the knowledge that we have of the quantum behaviour of the one electron that is found in a hydrogen atom to guide us towards an understanding of the behaviour of the many electrons that are found in more complicated atoms. Of course, you shouldn't expect to understand the full richness of atomic behaviour on the basis of a brief introduction to the hydrogen atom, but what you already know can be used to provide an insight into the behaviour of helium and lithium atoms (the two simplest atoms after hydrogen), and those atoms illustrate many of the general principles that govern the structure of more complicated atoms. This in turn opens up the field of chemistry. In Block 8 you will see that the chemical behaviour of atoms relies crucially on the way in which the electrons are arranged around the nucleus in each different element.

Activity 4.1 Electrons in atoms

This CD-ROM activity aims to develop your understanding of energy levels, quantum states and spectra, and the relationship between them. The rest of Section 4 assumes that you have completed this activity. ◀

What is it that makes the hydrogen atom, the He$^+$ ion and the Li^{2+} ion similar?

All of these have just a *single* bound electron. He$^+$ and Li^{2+} ions can therefore be described as **hydrogen-like ions**.

In Activity 4.1 you saw that the energy levels of a hydrogen-like ion with nuclear charge Ze are given by:

$$E_n = Z^2 \times \left(\frac{-13.60\,\text{eV}}{n^2} \right) \tag{4.1}$$

which differs from Equation 3.1 (the corresponding equation for the hydrogen atom) only by the factor of Z^2. Since $Z = 1$ for the hydrogen atom, the two equations are identical in that case, so Equation 4.1 is really just a generalization of Equation 3.1.

As you saw in Activity, 4.1, in the case of the helium ion, He$^+$, $Z = 2$, so Equation 4.1 implies that each value of E_n is Z^2, i.e. four, times larger than the corresponding value for the hydrogen atom. It also follows that the separation between any two energy levels in the He$^+$ ion will be four times greater than the separation between the corresponding levels in the hydrogen atom.

In Activity 4.1 you also saw that the electron clouds corresponding to a state with principal quantum number n in the He$^+$ ion have the same shape as those for the corresponding state of the hydrogen atom, but are scaled *down* by a factor of two. Speaking very loosely, all atoms or ions with just a single bound electron are very similar, except that the extra charge on the nucleus of the more massive ions tends to pull the electron in closer and speed it up. As noted earlier the electrical energy dominates the overall energy of the atom, so the smaller separation between the electron and the nucleus makes the energy of the state smaller, i.e. more negative, and the electron is more tightly bound.

Question 4.1   (a) The Be^{3+} ion, with atomic number $Z = 4$, has one bound electron. Use Equation 4.1 to calculate the energy corresponding to the ground state of this ion.

(b) The energy of the first excited state (i.e. $n = 2$) of the Be^{3+} ion turns out to be very close to the energy of the ground state of the one-electron helium ion He$^+$. Why is this? ◀

4.2   Atoms and ions with two electrons

There is *no* simple formula like Equation 3.1 for the energy levels of any neutral atom other than hydrogen. Quantum physics can predict the energy levels of the helium atom (for which $Z = 2$) to high precision, but it takes a lot of computer time to achieve this. Generally speaking, it takes even more computer time to determine the energy levels for atoms with three or more electrons.

Another point to note is that, for hydrogen atoms and hydrogen-like ions, the energy of each state is uniquely determined by just the principal quantum number n. All 2s and 2p excited states for instance have the same energy level in hydrogen. In atoms with two or more electrons, things are no longer that simple. Interactions between the electrons mean that the energy levels of each state depend on the other quantum numbers, such as l, as well as on n.

The reason for this increasing complexity is not particularly related to quantum physics. Similar complications would arise in attempts to use Newton's laws to predict the behaviour of the Solar System if it contained two planets that attracted each other as strongly as each is attracted to the Sun. (This so-called *three body problem* is one of the famous unsolved problems of physics.) In the case of the helium atom the analogous problem is to find the electron clouds for two electrons, in states of definite energy, when each electron is subject to the attractive influence of the nucleus *and* to the repulsive influence of the other electron. Just in case this doesn't already sound challenging enough, bear in mind that this is quantum physics, so the positions and speeds of both electrons will be indeterminate!

In the case of the hydrogen-like ions (in Activity 4.1) we can be quite prescriptive about the quantum state that is occupied by the single bound electron. If the ion is in its ground state, the electron occupies a 1s state, and if the ion is in an excited state, then the electron might occupy a 2s state, or a 2p state, or any of the excited states that were described at the end of Section 3. These states are not exactly like those of the hydrogen atom, but for these simple ions we can fit the electrons into 'hydrogen-like' states since the only thing that changes is the charge on the nucleus.

Now, when we come to atoms or ions with two bound electrons, such as He or Li^+, the state of the atom can once again be described in terms of the behaviour of the electrons. For instance a quantum state described by 1s 1s would indicate that an atom contains two electrons, each occupying something like a 1s state of a hydrogen-like atom. A quantum state described by 1s 2s would indicate that an atom contains two electrons, with one of them occupying a 1s hydrogen-like state and the other a 2s hydrogen-like state. But what are the energy levels corresponding to these quantum states?

Let's first think about the energy-level diagram for the helium atom, which has two electrons. The ground state of helium will be described by 1s 1s and so will correspond to two bound electrons, each occupying something like a 1s state of a hydrogen-like atom. To depict the energy-level diagram, we first need to decide where to position the zero of energy. In the case of the hydrogen atom, the zero was chosen to correspond to a state in which the electron just manages to escape from the nucleus. Figure 4.1 shows the energy-level diagram for the helium atom, and as you can see we've chosen the zero energy to correspond to the energy level for a helium nucleus (and two free electrons). The energy level corresponding to the ground state of singly ionized helium He^+ is also shown, with the value (-54.40 eV) you saw in Activity 4.1.

Figure 4.1 The energy-level diagram for the helium atom. This shows energy levels for the helium nucleus He^{2+} plus two free electrons, for the ground state of the He^+ ion plus one free electron, and for the ground state of the helium atom He.

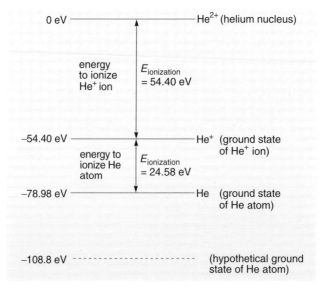

Now suppose, for a moment, that we could ignore the repulsion of the two electrons in the ground state of the helium atom. Then the ground-state energy would correspond to assigning principal quantum number $n = 1$ to each electron, and adding the energies associated with each.

○ Where would such a hypothetical ground state be?

○ You saw in Activity 4.1 that the ground state of the He⁺ ion with one bound electron is at an energy of −54.40 eV, so the hypothetical ground state of a helium atom with two bound electrons might be expected to be at an energy of $2 \times (-54.40\,\text{eV}) = -108.8\,\text{eV}$.

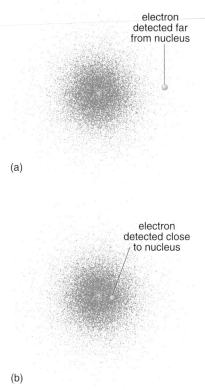

(a)

Figure 4.1 shows that, in reality, the true ground state of the helium atom is significantly higher, at an energy of −78.98 eV. To understand, qualitatively, why the true ground-state energy of Figure 4.1 is higher than the hypothetical ground state, with no interaction, it helps to think in terms of electron clouds. As shown in Figure 4.2a, there is some probability of finding one electron far from the nucleus. In this case the distant electron effectively experiences the electric force due to the He⁺ ion, with charge e. Conversely, as shown in Figure 4.2b, there is a probability of one electron being rather close to the nucleus, and hence experiencing the effect of the full nuclear charge, $2e$. This being the quantum world, all possibilities between these two extremes are allowed, and the typical charge experienced by each electron will be something between e and $2e$. The name given to this effect is **screening** and you can think of it as one electron neutralizing, or cancelling out, part of the charge of the nucleus. You saw in Activity 4.1 that the energies of the states depend strongly on the nuclear charge. So it should come as no surprise that, when one electron reduces the effective charge experienced by the other, the energy levels will change dramatically.

(b)

Figure 4.2 Two possible results of measuring the position of one electron in a helium atom. (a) An electron is detected far from the nucleus. Part of the charge of the nucleus is *screened* by the electron cloud of the other electron, so the net charge experienced by the distant electron is only e. (b) An electron is detected close the nucleus. The electron cloud of the other electron does not screen the nucleus, so the net charge experienced by the inner electron is the full $2e$. The effective charge experienced by either electron will be somewhere between these two extremes.

In the general case of a two-electron ion, with nuclear charge Ze, the 'effective' nuclear charge, determining the ground-state energy, lies somewhere between $(Z-1)e$, corresponding to complete screening of one unit of charge by an inner electron cloud, and Ze, corresponding to no screening.

Equation 4.1 gives the ground-state energy for any ion with just a single electron as $E_1 = Z^2 \times (-13.60\,\text{eV})$. A first estimate for the ground-state energy of a two-electron ion might be just twice this value, $E_{\text{est}} = 2 \times Z^2 \times (-13.60\,\text{eV})$. But as you've seen above, the effective charge experienced by each electron is not Ze but something between $(Z-1)e$ and Ze. Let's call this effective charge $Z_{\text{est}}e$. So a better estimate for the ground-state energy of a two-electron ion is:

$$E_{\text{est}} = 2 \times Z_{\text{est}}^2 \times (-13.60\,\text{eV}) \tag{4.2}$$

By making approximations to the difficult mathematics required to solve the Schrödinger equation, the value of Z_{est} which determines the effective nuclear charge experienced by two electrons bound to a nucleus of charge Ze is obtained as:

$$Z_{\text{est}} = Z - 0.312\,5 \tag{4.3}$$

To see how the estimate fares, set $Z = 2$, for the helium atom. In this case, $Z_{\text{est}} = 2 - 0.312\,5 = 1.687\,5$ and therefore

$$E_{\text{est}} = 2 \times (1.687\,5)^2 \times (-13.60\,\text{eV}) = -77.46\,\text{eV}$$

Comparing this with the experimental result of −78.98 eV (Figure 4.1), we see that the actual value lies only about 1.5 eV below the estimate.

Now, you have seen that the ground-state energy of the helium *atom* is −78.98 eV and that the ground-state energy of the helium *ion* is −54.40 eV. In order to turn an atom into an ion, the atom must be ionized. So the ionization energy of the helium atom is the energy required to remove one electron from the atom in its ground state. As shown on Figure 4.1, the energy required to do this corresponds to the energy of the helium *ion* ground state minus the energy of the helium *atom* ground state, $E_{ionization} = −54.40\,eV − (−78.98\,eV) = (78.98 − 54.40)\,eV = 24.58\,eV$. This is the *biggest* ionization energy for any neutral atom.

You are now in a position to make quantitative predictions about the ground-state energy and ionization energy of the singly ionized lithium ion, Li^+. This has two bound electrons and is therefore comparable to the helium atom. It too has a ground state denoted by 1s 1s, the only difference is its atomic number, $Z = 3$.

Question 4.2   (a) Use Equations 4.2 and 4.3 to obtain an estimate for the ground-state energy of the Li^+ ion.

(b) Use Equation 4.1 to calculate the ground-state energy of the Li^{2+} ion.

(c) Using the two values you have just calculated, what is the energy required in order to remove an electron from the ground state of the Li^+ ion and so turn it into a Li^{2+} ion? ◄

4.3   Atoms with three or more electrons

As you have just seen, it takes about 122 eV to remove the electron from a Li^{2+} ion, and it takes about 74 eV to remove one of the electrons from a Li^+ ion. However, it turns out that only about 5 eV is required to remove one of the electrons from a neutral Li atom. No singly ionized ion requires more energy than Li^+ to make it doubly ionized, yet the lithium atom itself is rather easily ionized, much more easily than either the helium atom or the hydrogen atom.

The key to understanding why this is so is to consider what happens when we add a third electron to the ground state of Li^+, to make a neutral lithium atom. As you saw in Section 3, there are only two quantum states that have quantum numbers $n = 1$ and $l = 0$, i.e. there are only two 1s states. We can think of these hydrogen-like states as though they can each be 'occupied' by a single electron. So the ground state of lithium cannot correspond to a quantum state of 1s 1s 1s.

The principle that bans the third electron from being in a similar state to the other two is a crucial result of quantum physics; it was suggested by Wolfgang Pauli (Figure 4.3).

> The Pauli **exclusion principle** bans any two electrons in the same atom from occupying the same quantum state.

Remember from Section 3 that for any value of n, there are two s states, six p states, ten d states, and so on. According to the exclusion principle, each of these states can accommodate only one electron.

So, since there are only two 1s states, the third electron in a lithium atom occupies a state something more like the 2s state of hydrogen shown in Figure 3.10. The ground state of the lithium atom can therefore be represented as 1s 1s 2s. The third electron in the lithium atom has principal quantum number $n = 2$, which makes it much more remote from the nucleus. Thus one of the three electrons in the lithium atom is rather

Figure 4.3   Wolfgang Pauli (1900–1958) studied at the University of Munich. While still an undergraduate he wrote a highly respected article explaining Einstein's recently formulated theory of general relativity. Despite this precocity, he shared the common difficulty of coming to terms with quantum physics, saying that 'I was not spared the shock which every physicist accustomed to the classical way of thinking experienced when he came to know Bohr's basic postulate of quantum theory for the first time.' Pauli also first suggested that a previously undetected particle, now called the neutrino, is produced in the β-decays of nuclei, as will be explained in Section 5.2.

weakly bound, since it experiences a net charge that is not much greater than the one unit of charge of the Li$^+$ ion, with the other two units of nuclear charge effectively screened by the other two, more tightly bound, electrons. A rough estimate of the ionization energy of the lithium atom would be somewhat greater than that for the 2s or 2p state of hydrogen, namely $\dfrac{13.60 \text{ eV}}{2^2}$ = 3.40 eV. In fact it is 5.39 eV, indicating that the other two electrons do not completely screen two units of nuclear charge.

As you have seen, for simple atoms such as He and Li we can be fairly prescriptive about the states occupied by the two or three electrons that we now have to consider. For the helium atom both electrons can occupy 1s states, so the ground state of helium is 1s 1s. For the lithium atom, you have seen that the ground state is 1s 1s 2s.

With more electrons, this notation soon gets unwieldy. To avoid this problem we now introduce a compact way of describing the organization of the electrons around a nucleus, referred to as the **electron configuration**. For the helium atom which has a ground state of 1s 1s, the electron configuration is written as 1s^2, and for the lithium atom which has a ground state of 1s 1s 2s, the electron configuration is written as 1s^2 2s^1. It is important to realize that the superscripts here *do not* refer to 'powers' of numbers, they are merely labels indicating the number of electrons that occupy the states specified by the n and l quantum numbers. In Block 8, you will learn to relate such descriptions of the electron configurations of atoms to the position of the elements in the Periodic Table.

number of electrons in each state

$1s^2 \, 2s^1$

value of n   *s means l = 0*

It is often quite convenient to think of electrons as 'filling up' successive **sub-shells** in the atom. For instance: the 1s sub-shell can accommodate two electrons since there are two 1s quantum states, the 2s sub-shell can accommodate two more electrons, and the 2p sub-shell can accommodate a further six electrons since there are six 2p quantum states. Sub-shells are filled in order of increasing energy so that the atom as a whole has the lowest possible energy level. Although such terminology is not entirely accurate, owing to the interactions between electrons, it provides a useful simplification. For atoms that contain several electrons the states are different from the 'hydrogen-like' quantum states that you saw in Activity 4.1. This is because the interactions between the electrons complicate matters, and so does the Pauli exclusion principle.

Question 4.3 (a) What do you suppose is the ground-state electron configuration for beryllium with four electrons?

(b) What will be the ground-state electron configuration for boron with five electrons?

(c) What is the largest number of electrons that can be accommodated by filling the 1s, 2s, and 2p sub-shells? ◀

We are now entering the realms of chemistry, and further exploration of electron configurations and sub-shell structure for the rest of the elements will be presented in Block 8. We conclude by emphasizing the remarkable fact that lithium is a highly reactive metal, but helium is an extremely inert (unreactive) gas. Yet the only difference between the two is that lithium atoms contain three electrons surrounding a nucleus containing three protons, whereas helium atoms have two electrons surrounding a nucleus with two protons. The difference in chemical properties is all due to the difference in the ionization energies of the two atoms, which in turn is due to the fact that quantum physics and the exclusion principle place a limit on the number of electrons in different states.

4.4 Summary of Section 4

Hydrogen-like ions have energy levels given by:

$$E_n = Z^2 \times \left(\frac{-13.60\,\text{eV}}{n^2} \right) \tag{4.1}$$

As a consequence of this: the energy levels of He⁺ ions are further apart than those of hydrogen atoms by a factor of four and the photon energies in the spectrum of He⁺ ions are greater than those of hydrogen atoms by a factor of four. The electron clouds for He⁺ ions are also more compact than those for hydrogen atoms by a factor of two.

In atoms and ions with two electrons, one electron will partially screen the charge on the nucleus from the other electron. This raises the energy levels above what would be predicted if there were no interaction between the electrons.

The Pauli exclusion principle bans any two electrons in the same atom from occupying the same quantum state. It plays a vital role in determining the way electrons are arranged in atoms. One consequence of the exclusion principle is that any s state can only accommodate two electrons. Lithium, with three electrons, therefore has the ground-state electron configuration $1s^2\,2s^1$, making it much easier to ionize than helium with the ground-state electron configuration $1s^2$.

It is often convenient to think of electrons as filling up successive sub-shells in an atom. Each sub-shell is characterized by a particular combination of n and l quantum numbers, and is only able to accommodate a certain number of electrons, equal to the number of quantum states with that particular combination of n and l.

Nuclear structure

5

We now travel further inside the atom to examine the quantum world of atomic nuclei. You know already, from Block 6, that nuclei have two building blocks: neutrons and protons, and these are referred to collectively as *nucleons*. It is different numbers of protons in nuclei that account for the different elements of the Periodic Table. One aim of this section is to show you how atoms can transform from one type to another.

Even though we are entering a new realm, be assured that there are many similarities between the quantum world of atoms and electrons, that you have just read about, and the quantum world of nuclei. For instance, as in the case of an atom, a nucleus can have only certain allowed energies. Quantum jumps occur between such energy levels, with the emission or absorption of photons. In the case of nuclei, these are gamma-ray (γ-ray) photons (γ is the Greek letter gamma). As Figure 2.8 shows, γ-ray photons have energies greater than about 1 MeV (remember, 1 MeV = 10^6 eV, see Box 2.1), i.e. a million times greater than those of a visible photon. (This is why we were able to ignore nuclear transitions in earlier sections when discussing emission and absorption of light.) Another similarity is that, as in the case of electrons in atoms, the positions and speeds of nucleons in nuclei are subject to indeterminacy, and their positions can be represented by probability clouds. The distinctive feature of nuclei is that the nucleons are confined in a volume that is less than 10^{-14} m in diameter, more than 10^4 times smaller than the diameter of an atom (Figure 1.5).

Just as atoms can make transitions between different quantum states, so too can nuclei. But the possibilities for changes in nuclei are far more varied than those open to electrons in atoms. The big difference is that nuclei can also transform from one element to another in a variety of nuclear 'decays'. (Decay processes were introduced in Block 6, Section 14.) In Activity 5.1 you will have access to a computer database of the properties of nuclei, and to information about nuclear decays, to help you investigate which nuclei exist and which of these are stable.

In all nuclear decays certain principles are obeyed, which we summarize briefly here.

- Electric charge is always conserved: the net charge of the products of a nuclear decay is the same as the net charge of the original nucleus.

- The mass number is conserved: the total number of nucleons in the products is the same as that in the original nucleus.

- As in all physical processes, energy is conserved. The one complication here though, is that since the energies involved in nuclear decays are so large, we need to take account of the relationship between energy and mass, suggested by Einstein, $E = mc^2$, that you first met in Block 5.

To begin your investigation of nuclear decays, we first revisit the α-decay process that you encountered at the end of Block 6.

5.1 α-decay

The α-particle is simply the nucleus of the helium atom ^4_2He, with mass number $A = 4$ and atomic number $Z = 2$. It consists of $Z = 2$ protons and $A - Z = 4 - 2 = 2$ neutrons. (The symbol N is often used to represent the number of neutrons.) It is a very tightly bound arrangement: this ground state for two protons and two neutrons has an energy that is about 28 MeV lower than the energy of the four free nucleons.

In some cases, it is energetically favourable for a nucleus of mass number A and atomic number Z to emit an α-particle, thereby producing a new nucleus, with mass number $A - 4$ and atomic number $Z - 2$. A case in point is the unstable isotope of uranium, $^{234}_{92}U$.

⬤ What does this notation indicate for the atomic number and mass number of a uranium nucleus?

◯ This indicates that the atomic number $Z = 92$, and the mass number $A = 234$.

So this isotope of uranium has 92 protons and $(234 - 92) = 142$ neutrons. It undergoes α-decay to produce an isotope of thorium, with 90 protons and 140 neutrons:

$$^{234}_{92}U \longrightarrow \, ^{230}_{90}Th + \, ^{4}_{2}He$$

Question 5.1   The thorium isotope produced in this α-decay undergoes a further four α-decays. What isotope of lead results? ◀

Both electric charge and mass number are conserved in an α-decay process since there is the same number of protons and neutrons in the products as in the original nucleus. But what of energy conservation? Well, nuclear decays will clearly involve changes in energy, much as the atomic transitions that you studied in earlier sections. For example, the α-decay of $^{234}_{92}U$ liberates 4.86 MeV of kinetic energy, carried away (almost exclusively) by the α-particle. We can write the decay as:

$$^{234}_{92}U \longrightarrow \, ^{230}_{90}Th + \, ^{4}_{2}He + 4.86\,MeV$$

In order to discover just where the 4.86 MeV of energy has appeared from, it is instructive to consider the masses of the nuclei involved. Accurate measurements of the masses of the α-particle and thorium nucleus reveal that their sum is *less* than the mass of the original uranium nucleus. In other words, some mass is 'lost' during the decay process:

$$(\text{mass of } ^{234}_{92}U) = (\text{mass of } ^{230}_{90}Th) + (\text{mass of } ^{4}_{2}He) + (8.66 \times 10^{-30}\,kg)$$

What has happened is that a mass of 8.66×10^{-30} kg has been converted into energy in the course of the decay. This can be explained using Einstein's famous equation for converting between mass and energy:

$$E = mc^2 \tag{5.1}$$

where c is the value of the speed of light. We can confirm that 8.66×10^{-30} kg is equivalent to 4.86 MeV as follows:

$$E = mc^2 = 8.66 \times 10^{-30}\,kg \times (3.00 \times 10^8\,m\,s^{-1})^2$$

$$= 7.79 \times 10^{-13}\,J$$

Now we showed in Box 2.1 that $1\,eV = 1.6 \times 10^{-19}$ J, or 1.60×10^{-19} J to three significant figures, so $1\,J = \dfrac{1\,eV}{1.60 \times 10^{-19}}$, and therefore

$$E = 7.79 \times 10^{-13} \times \frac{1\,eV}{1.60 \times 10^{-19}} = 4.86 \times 10^6\,eV$$

$$= 4.86\,MeV$$

So the equation $E = mc^2$ tells us that a mass of 8.66×10^{-30} kg is equivalent to 4.86 MeV of energy.

Now, as you can see from the example above, the mass loss in a nuclear decay is a rather cumbersome number when expressed in units of kilograms. For this reason, alternative mass units are often used instead. Equation 5.1 may be rearranged to give $m = \dfrac{E}{c^2}$ and this means that the units of mass are the same as the units of $\left(\dfrac{\text{energy}}{c^2} \right)$. In particular, since a mass of 8.66×10^{-30} kg is equivalent to an energy of 4.86 MeV, we can say that this mass is 4.86 MeV/c^2, and we can write:

$$(\text{mass of } {}^{234}_{92}\text{U}) = (\text{mass of } {}^{230}_{90}\text{Th}) + (\text{mass of } {}^{4}_{2}\text{He}) + 4.86 \text{ MeV}/c^2$$

So an energy of 4.86 MeV is liberated by mass loss of 4.86 MeV/c^2.

To appreciate how substantial this change in mass is, it helps to express the mass of the proton in the alternative mass units. The result is $m_p = 938$ MeV/c^2, or almost 1 GeV/c^2 (remember 1 GeV $= 10^9$ eV, see Box 2.1). So, in the α-decay above, the decrease in mass is 4.86 MeV/c^2 which is about 0.5% of the proton's mass, and hence about 0.002% of the mass of the original uranium nucleus, with $A = 234$. Nuclear masses have been determined to sufficient accuracy to confirm such effects. Their values will be provided in Activity 5.1, and from them you will be able to work out which decays are possible, and how much kinetic energy they liberate.

Question 5.2   (a) The naturally occurring radium isotope ${}^{226}_{88}\text{Ra}$ undergoes α-decay to the radon isotope ${}^{222}_{86}\text{Rn}$. The mass of the products is 4.87 MeV/c^2 less than the mass of the original nucleus. How much energy is liberated by the decay? (Note that you don't need to do any calculations to answer this question!)

(b) The naturally occurring isotope of protactinium ${}^{231}_{91}\text{Pa}$ undergoes α-decay to produce a nucleus of actinium ${}^{227}_{89}\text{Ac}$ and liberates 5.15 MeV of energy. By how much is the combined mass of the actinium nucleus and the α-particle less than the mass of the original protactinium nucleus? (Do *not* try to convert this mass into kilograms.) ◀

5.2   β-decay

We now turn our attention to the second mode of nuclear decay that you met at the end of Block 6, namely β-decay. As you may remember, the type of β-decay that you encountered there involves the emission of an *electron* from the nucleus of an atom. Perhaps the first question to address is where did that electron come from? Was it there in the first place? The answer is no; it is quite impossible for nuclei to 'contain' electrons. The electron is *created* by the decay, just as a photon is created when an atom makes a transition from a higher energy level to a lower energy level.

In order to see how the electron comes into existence, we consider a specific case, namely the β-decay of the lead isotope, ${}^{214}_{82}\text{Pb}$. Now, the electric charge of the lead nucleus is 82e since it contains 82 protons, and the electron emitted by the nucleus has a charge of $-e$. Since charge is conserved in all nuclear decay processes, the charge of the nucleus *before* the decay must be equal to the charge of the nucleus *after* the decay plus the charge of the electron that is emitted. Clearly, $82e =$ (charge of resultant nucleus) $+ (-e)$, so the charge of the resultant nucleus must be $83e$.

○ How many protons does the resultant nucleus contain? Using the Appendix to the Block 6 Study File, what element does it represent?

○ The resultant nucleus must contain 83 protons. From the Appendix, it is therefore a nucleus of the element bismuth ($Z = 83$).

So the resultant bismuth nucleus has one more proton than the original lead nucleus. But where has that proton come from? To answer that we must consider the mass number of the nucleus. Since mass number is also conserved in nuclear decays, the total number of nucleons (i.e. protons plus neutrons) in the resultant bismuth nucleus must be the same as in the original lead nucleus.

○ How many nucleons does the resultant bismuth nucleus contain, and what is the chemical symbol for this isotope?

○ It contains 214 nucleons — the same as the original lead nucleus. The resultant nucleus is therefore the bismuth isotope $^{214}_{83}\text{Bi}$.

Since the bismuth nucleus contains one more proton than the lead nucleus, but the same number of nucleons in total, it must contain one less neutron than the original lead nucleus. What has happened is that one of the neutrons in the lead nucleus has transformed into a proton, with the emission of an electron. Transformations between neutrons and protons lie at the heart of all β-decay processes.

For reasons that will become clearer in Block 11, another particle is created in the β-decay process too. It is called the **electron antineutrino** and it has zero electric charge. Creation of an electron and an electron antineutrino occurs in what is called **β⁻-decay** (beta-minus decay), the minus sign indicating that the electron is negatively charged. The overall decay process for this lead isotope is therefore:

$$^{214}_{82}\text{Pb} \longrightarrow \, ^{214}_{83}\text{Bi} + e^- + \overline{\nu}_e$$

The rather clumsy symbol $\overline{\nu}_e$ represents an electron antineutrino, where ν is the Greek letter *nu* (pronounced 'new'). The subscript e indicates that it is associated with an electron, and the bar over the top of the letter indicates that it is an antimatter particle (see Box 5.1, *Matter and antimatter*).

Question 5.3 A nucleus of the unstable nitrogen isotope $^{16}_{7}\text{N}$ undergoes β⁻-decay. Write down an expression for this nuclear decay, indicating which nucleus is formed as a result. ◀

Box 5.1 *Matter and antimatter*

The electron antineutrino is the first example of **antimatter** encountered in this course, and a second — the positron — will be introduced shortly. They are the antiparticles of the electron neutrino and the electron, respectively. Now although you may have thought antimatter to be the stuff of science fiction, it is a very real feature of the Universe. Antimatter particles have the same mass as their matter counterparts but their other attributes, such as charge, have the opposite sign. All matter particles have corresponding antimatter counterparts.

$\Rightarrow$

The antimatter counterpart of the electron, the positron, was discovered in 1932. More recently, in 1996, atoms of antihydrogen were created, consisting of antiprotons bound to positrons. Nowadays antimatter particles can be created routinely in high-energy particle accelerators, but it is difficult stuff to control! If matter and antimatter come into contact with each other they will mutually annihilate producing a large amount of energy.

Our Universe today seems to consist almost exclusively of matter particles rather than antimatter. However, as you will see in Block 11, the early Universe was not such a one-sided place.

The process described above is only half of the story as far as β-decay is concerned. There is a very closely related process, called **β⁺-decay** (beta-plus decay), in which a positively charged particle, called the **positron**, is created, along with an **electron neutrino**, which has zero charge. In this process, a proton in the original nucleus transforms into a neutron, so *decreasing* the atomic number by one. A nucleus that undergoes β⁺-decay is the unstable oxygen isotope $^{14}_{8}O$ which transforms into a stable nitrogen isotope $^{14}_{7}N$. The decay in this case can be represented as:

$$^{14}_{8}O \longrightarrow {}^{14}_{7}N + e^+ + \nu_e$$

Here, the symbol e^+ is used to represent the positron (also known as an antielectron) and ν_e is the electron neutrino. Box 5.1 explains the relationship between some of these particles.

Question 5.4   A nucleus of the unstable phosphorus isotope $^{30}_{15}P$ undergoes β⁺-decay. Write down an expression for this decay process, indicating which nucleus is formed as a result. ◀

Question 5.5   Write a few sentences to compare and contrast the processes of β⁻- and β⁺-decay. ◀

5.3   γ-decay

The final type of nuclear decay that we consider here is **γ-decay**. In contrast to the processes of α- and β-decay, this involves no change in the numbers of neutrons and protons. γ-decay occurs when a nucleus finds itself in an excited state. A quantum jump down to the ground state, with the same number of neutrons and protons, is accompanied by the emission of a photon, as with transitions in atoms. This time however, the photon energy is around a million time larger — it is a γ-ray photon. Such excited states of nuclei may be created as a result of α-decay or β-decay processes, or by the collisions of nuclei at high kinetic energies.

Question 5.6   The unstable isotope of caesium, $^{137}_{55}Cs$, undergoes β⁻-decay to produce an excited state of the barium isotope, $^{137}_{56}Ba$. The barium nucleus then decays to its ground state with the emission of a γ-ray photon of energy 662 keV. What are the atomic number and mass number of the barium nucleus *after* the γ-decay? ◀

Activity 5.1   Nucleons in nuclei

Now is the time to study the CD-ROM 'Nucleons in nuclei'. This will allow you to investigate which nuclei are stable, and to look at the random nature of radioactive decay processes. ◀

5.4   Summary of Section 5

A convenient way of displaying all the known *nuclides* is as a chart of the number of neutrons, N, against the number of protons (the atomic number), Z. The chart shows a thin ribbon of stable nuclides, bending slowly upwards as the number of neutrons progressively outruns the number of protons. This is surrounded by a wide band of unstable nuclides. Pairing of both neutrons and protons is favoured: in stable nuclides, neutrons are usually found in pairs, and nuclides in which protons are paired tend to be more abundant.

The most massive nuclides can be split into roughly equal halves, in a process known as *fission*. Sometimes this happens spontaneously and excess neutrons are often released in such fissions, which can give rise to a chain reaction.

In all nuclear decays, electric charge, mass number A and energy are conserved. Because of the high energies involved, we must take account of the conversion between mass and energy, expressed by

$$E = mc^2 \qquad\qquad\qquad (5.1)$$

It is often useful to express the masses of particles in units of MeV/c^2 or GeV/c^2, to emphasize the energy changes that occur.

There are a total of five types of nuclear decay or transition:

- α-decay in which helium nuclei are emitted;
- β⁻-decay in which a neutron converts into a proton with the emission of an electron and an electron antineutrino;
- β⁺-decay in which a proton converts into a neutron with the emission of a positron and an electron neutrino;
- *electron capture* in which a proton captures an electron so turning into a neutron;
- γ-decay in which a nucleus in an excited state makes a transition to a lower energy level, accompanied by the emission of a γ-ray photon.

A useful quantity to use when deciding whether a particular nuclide can decay is its *mass excess*. A three-dimensional chart of N against Z, with the vertical dimension representing mass excess, traces out a valley-shaped surface, with the stable nuclides along the bottom. Nuclides up the sides of the valley are unstable, and decay to nuclides on or closer to the valley floor.

In the process of radioactive decay, a plot of either the count rate, or the number of nuclei remaining, against time is *exponential* in shape. The graph falls by a factor of two for every *half-life* that elapses. The half-life is therefore the time for half the initial number of nuclei to decay. A graph of the count rate against the remaining number of radioactive nuclei is a straight line. This shows that the probability for a given nucleus to decay (in, say, the next second) remains constant. So these decay process are intrinsically unpredictable, event by event, yet follow a wonderfully simple rule when one studies large numbers of decays: the radioactivity is proportional to the number of excited nuclei that remain. Nuclei have no past: they never grow old; they either stay exactly the same, or change dramatically.

Fundamental particles

6

Half a century ago, the account of subatomic structure would have ended here. But now a third layer of structure is known: it is believed that protons and neutrons are composed of particles known as quarks. In this section we will be looking at an area which is at the forefront of scientific research today. Our aim is nothing less than an understanding of the fundamental constituents from which the Universe is built.

So far in this block you have met four types of subatomic particle: electrons, electron neutrinos, protons and neutrons, along with their antiparticles in some cases. Over the last 50 years or so, experiments have revealed that other subatomic particles exist, and that those mentioned above are merely the common representatives of two distinct classes of particle, namely leptons and hadrons. We now look at these in turn in order to complete the final leg of our journey to 'take the world apart'.

6.1 Leptons

Electrons (e^-) and electron neutrinos (ν_e), together with their antiparticles, are believed to be **fundamental particles**. By fundamental, we mean that there is no evidence that they are composed of smaller or simpler constituents. Furthermore, two more particles, with the same charge as the electron only rather heavier, were discovered in 1936 and 1975. The first is known as the muon (represented by μ^-, the Greek letter *mu*, which rhymes with 'cue') which is about 200 times heavier than the electron. The second is called the tauon (represented by τ^-, the Greek letter *tau*, which rhymes with 'cow') which is about 3 500 times heavier than the electron. The superscript minus signs on the electron, muon and tauon indicate that these particles all have a negative electric charge of $-e = -1.60 \times 10^{-19}$ C. Like the electron, the muon and tauon each has an associated neutrino: the muon neutrino (ν_μ) and the tauon neutrino (ν_τ). It is not yet known what the masses of the three types of neutrino are; indeed they may even have zero mass.

These six fundamental particles are collectively referred to as **leptons** — they are listed in Table 6.1 along with their electric charge. The six different types are often rather whimsically referred to as different *flavours* of lepton, and the three pairs of particles are often referred to as three *generations* of leptons.

Table 6.1 Six flavours of lepton.

	1st generation	2nd generation	3rd generation
leptons with charge $Q = -e$	e^-	μ^-	τ^-
leptons with charge $Q = 0$	ν_e	ν_μ	ν_τ

To each lepton there corresponds an **antilepton** with opposite charge but with the same mass. These are denoted by the symbols e^+, μ^+, τ^+ for the charged leptons and $\bar{\nu}_e$, $\bar{\nu}_\mu$, $\bar{\nu}_\tau$ for the neutral leptons. We shall have more to say about the three generations of leptons in Block 11.

6.2 Quarks

The other subatomic particles that you have so far met — protons and neutrons — are examples of **hadrons**. Although the *only* hadrons existing around us in the everyday world are protons and neutrons (these are the most stable examples of hadrons), many more types of hadron can be created in high-energy collisions of nucleons. Such reactions are common in the upper atmosphere, where high-energy protons from outer space (known as cosmic-ray protons) collide with nuclei of nitrogen and oxygen, smashing them apart and creating new hadrons. Since the 1960s, such reactions have been closely studied under controlled conditions in high-energy physics laboratories, where protons and electrons are accelerated to high kinetic energies using very high voltages, and then made to collide.

The hadrons occur with distinctive patterns of masses, charges, and other properties, and so form a sort of new Periodic Table, as extensive as that drawn up by Mendeléev. This proliferation of particles indicates that hadrons are composed of more fundamental particles, just as the Periodic Table of the elements indicates that atoms have an underlying structure. Fortunately, it will not be necessary for you to dwell on (let alone remember) the names and properties of all the hadrons, because there is a straightforward description for building them from particles that *are* believed to be fundamental, namely from **quarks** and **antiquarks**.

There are six flavours of quark, labelled (for historical reasons) by the letters u, d, c, s, t and b, which stand for up, down, charm, strange, top and bottom. Their charges, in units of the proton charge, e, are listed in Table 6.2. Like the leptons, the six quarks are often grouped into three generations, on the basis of their mass.

Table 6.2 Six flavours of quark.

	1st generation	2nd generation	3rd generation
quarks with charge $Q = +\frac{2}{3}e$	u	c	t
quarks with charge $Q = -\frac{1}{3}e$	d	s	b

To each quark, there corresponds an antiquark, with the opposite charge and the same mass. These are denoted by $\bar{u}$, $\bar{d}$, $\bar{c}$, $\bar{s}$, $\bar{t}$ and $\bar{b}$.

The **up quarks** and **down quarks** are the constituents of protons and neutrons, and along with their antiquark counterparts are the least massive of all the quarks. The charm and strange quarks and antiquarks are more massive than the up and down quarks, and the top and bottom quarks and antiquarks are more massive still. The large masses of these 2nd and 3rd generation quarks are the reason why high-energy particle accelerators are required to produce them. In order to create this amount of mass, a large amount of kinetic energy must be supplied in accordance with Equation 5.1 ($E = mc^2$). In fact, top quarks were first detected in the period 1994–5. They have masses nearly 200 times that of the proton.

Quarks and antiquarks have *never* been observed in isolation. They only seem to occur bound together inside hadrons. In fact there are three recipes for building hadrons from quarks, and these are shown in Figure 6.1.

A hadron can consist of:

> three quarks (in which case it is called a **baryon**);
>
> three antiquarks (in which case it is called an **antibaryon**);
>
> one quark and one antiquark (in which case it is called a **meson**).

As an example of this, the proton is a baryon, so it is composed of three quarks, and as mentioned above, it is composed of up and down quarks only. Now, the proton has charge $Q = +e$ and the only way that three up or down quarks can be combined to make this net charge is by combining two up quarks with a down quark. So the quark content of a proton is (uud), giving a charge $Q = +\frac{2}{3}e + \frac{2}{3}e - \frac{1}{3}e = +e$.

Question 6.1 Following the example described above, determine the quark content of a neutron. (*Hint*: Remember the charge of a neutron is zero, and it too is composed of three up or down quarks.) ◄

Antiparticles (see Box 5.1) of the proton and neutron are composed of antiquarks. In each case the antiparticle is composed of the corresponding combination of antiquarks, i.e. u is replaced by $\bar{u}$, and d is replaced by $\bar{d}$.

Question 6.2 What are the constituents of (a) an antiproton and (b) an antineutron? In each case calculate the charge of the resulting antiparticle by adding up the charges of the constituent antiquarks. ◄

This tally of six leptons and six quarks, each with their own antiparticles, may seem like a huge number of fundamental particles. However, don't let this put you off. Everything around us is made up of merely the first generation of each type, namely electrons, up quarks and down quarks, with electron neutrinos being created in β-decays. This slimmed down total of four particles is all that you need to remember. The second generation of leptons (μ^- and ν_μ) and the second generation of quarks (c and s), the third generation of leptons (τ^- and ν_τ) and the third generation of quarks (t and b), have exactly the same properties as their first generation counterparts except that they are more massive. Quite why nature decided to repeat her invention three times over is not currently understood.

6.3 High-energy reactions

As an example of the high-energy reactions that can occur, when a proton with kinetic energy of the order of 1 GeV collides with a nucleon, new hadrons, called **pions**, can be created. In such processes, some of the proton's kinetic energy is converted into mass, via the familiar equation $E = mc^2$, and so appears in the form of new particles. The pions that are created come in three varieties: π^+ with positive charge $+e$, π^- with negative charge $-e$, and a neutral π^0 with zero charge. (π^+, π^- and π^0 are read as 'pi-plus', 'pi-minus' and 'pi-zero', respectively.) Their masses are each around $140\,\mathrm{MeV}/c^2$, so 140 MeV of kinetic energy is required in order to create each pion.

Pions are examples of mesons and so are composed of a quark and an antiquark. In fact, pions are the least massive mesons and (like protons and neutrons) are composed of up and down quarks. To get a positive charge on π^+ we need the combination ($u\bar{d}$), with charge $Q = +\frac{2}{3}e + \frac{1}{3}e = +e$.

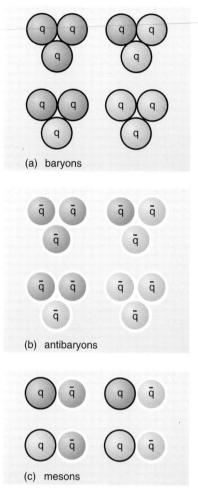

(a) baryons

(b) antibaryons

(c) mesons

Figure 6.1 The three recipes for building hadrons from quarks. Quarks and antiquarks with a charge of $\pm\frac{2}{3}e$ are shown in purple, those with a charge of $\pm\frac{1}{3}e$ are shown in orange (see Table 6.2). The symbol q represents a quark, and these are shown with black borders, and $\bar{q}$ represents an antiquark, shown with white borders. (a) Possible combinations making a baryon, (b) possible combinations making an antibaryon, (c) possible combinations making a meson.

Question 6.3 What is the quark–antiquark content of the negatively charged pion, π^-? ◀

But now there arises an interesting question about π^0: is it ($u\bar{u}$) or ($d\bar{d}$)? Each possibility follows the rules, and each produces zero charge.

The general principle of quantum physics seems to be that 'whatever is not strictly forbidden will be found to occur'. Each possibility is allowed; each is found to occur. But that does not mean that there are two types of π^0. It means that if we ask nature, in a suitable experiment, what is the content of π^0, sometimes we get one answer, sometimes the other. We have seen such things before in the quantum world. When studying atoms, it is only the act of measurement that forces one of the possible outcomes for the location of an electron. When studying some subatomic particles, the very notion of what something is made of is subject to the same indeterminacy, until we ask. It is then subject to the same regularity of probabilities when we do. Satisfyingly, experiments to determine the quark–antiquark content of π^0, by a study of its interactions, give one answer 50% of the time, and the alternative answer the other 50%.

6.4 Strong and weak interactions

At a subnuclear level, interactions between particles can be characterized into two sorts: **strong interactions** and **weak interactions**. We shall have more to say about these in Block 11, but for now note the following.

At a fundamental level, quarks and antiquarks interact via the so-called strong interaction. As a result they cluster together into triplets (baryons and antibaryons) or quark–antiquark pairs (mesons) (Figure 6.1). A subsidiary effect is that these hadrons can then interact with each other via a residual, or 'left over', strong interaction. One result of this is that protons and neutrons bind together to form stable nuclei, as illustrated in Figure 6.2a. There is an analogy here with atoms and molecules, shown in Figure 6.2b. Electrons and nuclei interact via the electrical force of attraction to form stable atoms. The residual electrical force that is 'left over' then enables atoms to bind together to make molecules.

Figure 6.2 (a) The strong interaction binds quarks together inside nucleons. A residual strong interaction is then responsible for binding protons and neutrons together to make stable nuclei. (b) Similarly, the electrical interaction binds electrons and nuclei together to make atoms. A residual electrical interaction is then responsible for binding atoms together to make molecules (you will learn more about this in Block 8).

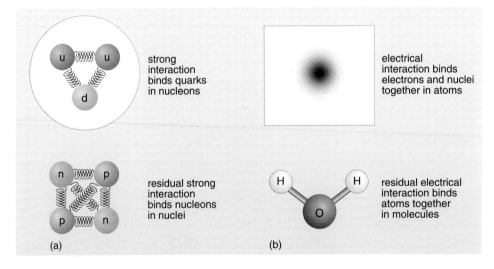

Strong interactions, such as those producing pions discussed above, involve hadrons, but not leptons. In a strong interaction, quark–antiquark pairs can be created out of raw energy. As long as energy and charge are conserved, anything is allowed! You will meet examples of this type of interaction in Activity 6.1. As you will see there, the strong interactions of nucleons and pions can be understood, in qualitative terms, as the rearrangement of quarks and antiquarks between hadrons, allowing for the possibility that a quark may annihilate its antiquark, or be created along with it. An important result of such reactions is that isolated quarks or antiquarks are *never* observed. They *always* occur in triplets (baryons and antibaryons) or in quark–antiquark pairs (mesons).

The quark model also allows us to obtain a deeper understanding of the β-decay process that you met in Section 5. This is an example of a so-called weak interaction. As you saw earlier, all β⁻- and β⁺-decays of nuclei involve transformations either from a neutron to a proton or vice versa. Now, you saw above that a neutron has the quark composition (udd) whilst a proton has the composition (uud). So these transformations in turn derive ultimately from changes of identity of up and down quarks occurring within nucleons, within nuclei, within atoms. This process will be explored further in Activity 6.1.

Activity 6.1   Quarks

This CD-ROM activity will allow you to investigate both strong and weak interactions at the level of nuclei, nucleons and quarks. You will also be able to see how different hadrons are built from quarks. ◄

Question 6.4   There is a hadron, formed in the collision of a pion and a nucleon, with charge $Q = +2e$. How can a single pion combine with a single nucleon to produce nothing but this new hadron? Is it a baryon, an antibaryon or a meson? ◄

In conclusion, just as electrons, protons and neutrons simplify the elements to their essentials, so a new layer of apparent complexity can be understood by the quark model. However, there is a crucial difference. If one hits an atom hard enough, electrons come out. If one hits a nucleus hard enough, nucleons come out. But if one hits a nucleon hard, with another nucleon, quarks do not come out. Instead the kinetic energy is transformed into the mass of new hadrons.

6.5   Summary of Section 6

The electron and the electron neutrino are examples of leptons. There are six flavours of lepton in total, all of which are believed to be fundamental particles.

There are also six flavours of quark. The least massive are the up quarks and the down quarks. Quarks, like leptons, are believed to be fundamental particles. Unlike leptons, they have never been observed in isolation.

Hadrons are composite particles made of quarks and antiquarks. Combinations of three quarks are called baryons, combinations of three antiquarks are called antibaryons, and combinations consisting of a quark and an antiquark are called mesons.

Nucleons (protons and neutrons) are merely special cases of baryons. Protons have the quark composition (uud) and neutrons have the quark composition (udd). Pions are examples of mesons, and are also composed of up and down quarks and antiquarks.

Strong interactions operate between quarks and between the composite particles (hadrons) that are made of quarks. Leptons do not participate in strong interactions.

Reactions involving strong interactions may be interpreted as the rearrangement of quarks between hadrons, accompanied by the creation, or annihilation, of quark–antiquark pairs.

Weak interactions, such as β-decay, involve the transformation of one flavour of quark into another flavour, with the emission of lepton–antilepton pairs.

7 Understanding light

In the block so far, we have largely been concerned with light as a tool for understanding about atoms, but from here on, we deal with light in its own right. First we clarify just what we mean by light, and then move on to look at how its properties may be measured.

7.1 What is light?

In 1873 James Clerk Maxwell proposed a unified theory of electricity and magnetism and deduced that light itself is an *electromagnetic* phenomenon. His theory showed that the passage of light (also called its propagation), from the source that emits it to the detector that absorbs it, is beautifully accounted for using the ideas of waves.

However, in Section 2 you saw that the quantum description of the interaction of light with matter was phrased in terms of photons. These particles of light have a certain amount of energy, referred to as a quantum. The question at issue here is: does the quantum description of the interaction of light with matter mean that there is something seriously wrong with the electromagnetic wave description?

The short answer is: no. Physicists and engineers can largely forget about quantum physics when predicting how light will pass through lenses and prisms, or the diffraction grating that you will learn to use in Section 10. If you ask what light is like, the answer you get depends crucially on the type of question. If you ask about propagation — getting from one place to another — the answer is 'wave-like'. If you ask about interaction with matter — creating or detecting light — the answer is 'particle-like': the quantized energy levels force light to be emitted and absorbed as photons.

So what is light *really* like? Quite simply, it is like light, namely:

> Light propagates like a wave and interacts like a particle.

For some people this is disturbing. Why can't light make up its mind? For others, it is rather a comfort that two ideas, derived from the macroscopic world of things like waves on water and bullets hitting targets, should *both* be of help in understanding something that is so vital to our well-being and to our understanding of the natural world.

So far we have used the language of photons, since we were concerned with the emission and absorption of light. One crucial omission has occurred: no details were given about how photon energies were assigned to the different colours in the spectrum, shown in Figure 2.6. That will be remedied in Sections 8–10, where you will combine the wave and photon pictures of light to determine photon energies from experimental measurements of wave-like propagation.

Before studying the properties of light, we recap on what you learned about spectra in Section 2 and introduce a new way of representing them.

7.2 Measuring spectra

You saw in Section 2 that when atoms make transitions between different quantum states, such that the atoms *lose* energy, then photons are *emitted*. Each photon carries a certain amount of energy, the magnitude of which depends on the difference in energy between two energy levels of the atom concerned. Since the atom is allowed to exist only in certain quantum states, each with a specific energy level, only photons with particular energies are emitted. The distribution of the photons according to their energy, shown for example in the top half of Figure 7.1a, is known as an emission spectrum of the atoms involved. The bright, coloured lines indicate the presence of photons with particular energies, and these energies correspond to the difference in energy between certain allowed states of the atoms. Dark regions indicate that no photons with these energies are emitted — there are no atomic energy levels separated by these particular energy values.

Alternatively, when atoms *absorb* photons, they again make transitions between different quantum states, but this time such that the atoms *gain* energy. So if photons with a range of energies are directed at particular atoms, only photons with certain energies are absorbed. The remaining photons that emerge are distributed according to their energy as shown in the top half of Figure 7.1b, and this is known as an absorption spectrum of the atoms involved. The dark lines indicate an absence of photons with particular energies, and these energies correspond to differences between allowed energy levels of the atoms involved. Bright regions indicate that no photons with these energies are absorbed — there are no atomic energy levels separated by these particular energy values.

Up to now in the block we have represented all spectra pictorially in the manner of the top half of Figures 7.1a and b. However, to illustrate things more quantitatively, we need a method of plotting a spectrum as a graph. The equivalent graphs of these spectra are shown in the bottom half of Figures 7.1a and b. For the horizontal axis, we take the photon energy, E_{ph}. For the vertical axis, it is conventional to take the power per unit area that is carried by the light in a small range of photon energies centred on E_{ph}. This is known as the **intensity** and it is related to the *number* of photons of a particular energy that are present. A plot of the intensity against the

Figure 7.1 Examples of (a) an emission spectrum and (b) an absorption spectrum. The top half of the figure shows pictorial representations of spectra in the energy range corresponding to visible light. The bottom half shows these same spectra, but converted into graphs of intensity against photon energy, known as spectral distributions. You can think of the spectral distributions as representing how dark or bright the spectra appear at a given energy: the brighter the spectrum, the more intense the light registered in the spectral distribution, at a given energy. The two ways of representing a particular emission spectrum or absorption spectrum are entirely equivalent to each other. However, the spectral distributions are more quantitative, since they show not only where the emission lines and absorption lines occur, but just how intense the light is in each part of the spectrum.

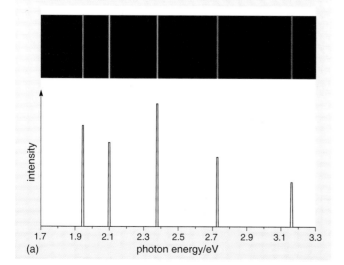

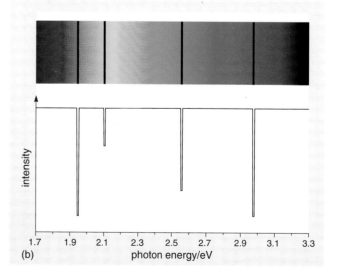

photon energy, like those shown in the bottom half of Figures 7.1a and b, is called a **spectral distribution**. It shows, quantitatively, how the energy carried by the light is distributed between different parts of the spectrum.

Continuous spectra, mentioned earlier in Section 2, can also be represented as graphs, and some examples are shown in Figure 7.2. These spectral distributions are produced by a metal that is heated to the temperatures shown. The 'glowing balls' in Figure 1.3 and the cooker plate and bulb filament in Figure 2.13 emit continuous spectra with similar spectral distributions to these.

Figure 7.2 Continuous spectral distributions of radiation emitted from a heated metal at temperatures of 2 000 °C and 3 000 °C.

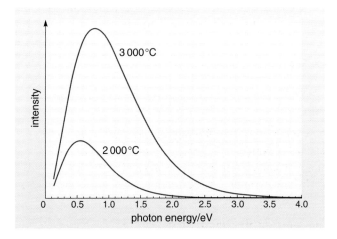

At what photon energy does the peak intensity occur for each spectrum in Figure 7.2?

The peak intensity of the spectrum emitted by a metal at 2 000 °C occurs at about 0.5 eV. The peak intensity of the spectrum emitted by a metal at 3 000 °C occurs at about 0.8 eV.

Since the peak intensities of these spectra occur at energies of less than 2 eV, these heated metals emit most of their radiation in the infrared part of the spectrum. However, there is also some emission in the region between 2 eV and 3 eV — the visible part of the spectrum. This is why a conventional light bulb (whose tungsten filament reaches a temperature of about 2 500 °C) produces (some) light (see Figure 2.13). Notice though that most of the radiation produced by a conventional light bulb is 'wasted' since it emerges in the infrared part of the spectrum. In Section 10 you will investigate the properties of so-called 'energy saver' light bulbs, and see why they are so named.

In fact, many objects produce continuous spectra whose distributions have similar shapes to those shown in Figure 7.2. These spectral distributions depend *only* on the temperature of the object, not its composition. The important point to note about such spectra is that at higher temperatures, the peak intensity occurs at higher energies. You have already seen graphs similar to those in Figure 7.2 back in Block 2, where the emission spectra of the Sun and Earth were compared. The surface of the Sun has a temperature of almost 6 000 °C, and its spectrum has a similar shape to those in Figure 7.2. However, the peak intensity of the Sun's spectrum occurs at higher energies — towards the visible part of the spectrum — simply because the Sun is hotter. We shall consider such continuous spectra again in Block 11.

Question 7.1 Using information from Section 2 and Figure 7.2, make rough sketches of the spectral distributions corresponding to:

(a) light from a sodium street lamp;

(b) light from a tungsten filament light bulb, after it has passed through sodium vapour. ◀

As you saw in Section 2, by making measurements on spectra such as those in Figure 7.1, important quantitative data may be determined concerning photon energies and the energy levels of atoms. One aim of the remaining sections is to show you just how measurements of photon energies are obtained. In fact, by the end of the block you will have made measurements of photon energies for yourself.

7.3 Summary of Section 7

Light propagates like a wave, but it interacts with matter as though it is composed of a stream of particles, known as photons.

Emission spectra are produced when atoms emit photons with specific energies that correspond to the difference in energy between two energy levels of the atoms concerned. Absorption spectra are produced when atoms absorb photons with specific energies that correspond to the difference in energy between two energy levels of the atoms concerned.

Spectra may be plotted as graphs of intensity against photon energy. Such a graph is referred to as a spectral distribution.

The continuous spectral distributions emitted by many hot objects have similar shapes. The higher the temperature of the object, the higher the energy at which the peak intensity in the spectral distribution occurs.

8 Light as a wave

In the first part of this section we will explain what we mean by waves and develop some of the terminology that is used to describe them. After this you will watch a video that will show you some examples of waves, and will extend the discussion to look at one of the most important features of their propagation — a phenomenon known as diffraction.

8.1 What is a wave?

We have told you that light travels from place to place as though it were a wave. But just what is meant by the word 'wave'? You were introduced to the idea of seismic waves in Block 3 and have already briefly met electromagnetic waves in Block 2. As a result of these earlier encounters you may already be familiar with some of the words that are used to describe a wave's properties. However, since waves are such an important concept, it is worth spending a little time now to get to grips fully with their key features and we take the opportunity here to revisit some concepts.

A **wave** may be defined as a *periodic*, or regularly repeating, disturbance that transports *energy* from one place to another. For instance, a stone dropped into the centre of a pond generates waves on the surface of the water which travel outwards and eventually cause a cork at the edge of the pond to bob up and down with a regular motion (see Block 2, Figure 5.2). Similarly, a sudden motion of part of the Earth's crust generates seismic waves which travel through the Earth, and may cause damage to buildings some distance away on the surface. Another image that the word 'wave' often conjures up is that of water waves on the sea, as shown in Figure 8.1.

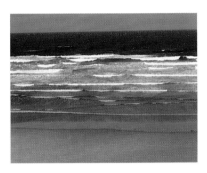

Figure 8.1 Waves on the sea.

If you've ever stood on a beach you will have seen or heard waves break onto the shore with a fairly regular time interval between each 'crash' and the next. Each crash represents one wave crest breaking onto the shore and the time interval between two of them is known as the **period** of the wave. In general, the period of a wave may be defined as the time between one part of the wave profile (say the crest) passing a fixed point in space and the *next* identical part of the wave profile (the next crest) passing the same fixed point. In the example here, the fixed point is the shoreline.

- What is the time interval between one *trough* of a wave and the next trough passing a fixed point?

- Since the troughs are spaced regularly between the crests, this time interval is also equal to the period of the wave.

Indeed, *any* point on the profile of a wave can be used as a 'marker' when measuring the wave's period. The important thing is that the time interval between two successive, *similar* points on the wave is used. Whether these successive points are both crests or both troughs, or both some, similar, intermediate point is irrelevant — in each case the time interval will be the period of the wave.

As well as being periodic with time, a wave is also periodic as far as its spatial extent is concerned. The word wave is often used to describe a *single* crash onto the beach, but it really refers to the entire sequence of crests and troughs, stretching away into the distance. The distance between one wave crest and the next is known as the **wavelength** of the wave (Figure 8.2). In general, the wavelength of a wave is defined as the distance between one part of the wave profile, at a particular instant in time, and the *next* identical part of the wave profile at the same instant in time — two adjacent crests of the wave are a convenient pair of locations to use for this definition, although any pair of similar points will do.

○ What is the distance between two adjacent *troughs* of a wave?

○ By a similar argument to that used when discussing the period of a wave, the distance between two adjacent troughs is the same as the distance between two adjacent crests. So, this distance is clearly also equal to the wavelength of the wave.

Question 8.1   Try the following thought experiment. Imagine that you are standing on a beach and watching wave crests break on the seashore.

(a) If the wavelength suddenly becomes larger (i.e. the wave crests are further apart than before), but the wave continues travelling at the same speed, what happens to the period of the wave?

(b) If, instead, the waves suddenly begin travelling more quickly across the sea, but with the same wavelength as before, what happens to the period of the wave? ◀

You will probably have noticed that the definitions for the period and wavelength of a wave are rather similar. The period is a time interval and refers to instances separated in *time*; the wavelength is a distance and refers to points separated in *space*. The relationship between them is clearly related to the *speed* at which the wave is moving — and that should come as no surprise since speed is the usual way of relating distances and times. The video 'Making waves' which you will watch in Activity 8.1 will quantify this relationship and develop the first key equation that describes the propagation of waves.

So much for the periodicity of waves; what of the assertion that they transport energy from one place to another? Again, waves on the sea provide a convenient example in the first instance. Waves may be generated far out to sea by winds, where energy is imparted to the wave and transported by it until the wave finally breaks on the shore, and the energy is released.

○ What is the evidence for this release of energy when a wave breaks on the seashore?

○ When the wave breaks, kinetic energy is imparted to pebbles and other debris, so causing them to move. Also, you hear the sound of the crash, which is further evidence for the release of energy.

How does the energy transported by a wave on the sea depend on the properties of the wave? Well, again your experience will probably tell you that if the vertical distance between the trough and crest of a wave is greater (i.e. if the waves are 'higher') then more energy is released as they crash onto the shore. During a storm, waves on the sea tend to be very high, and often a great deal of damage is done on shore. Energy is required to damage breakwaters and sea defences, so clearly higher waves carry more

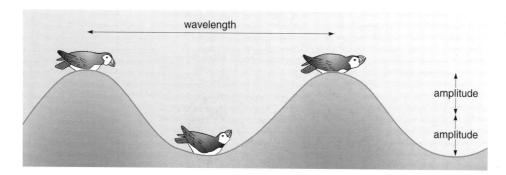

Figure 8.2   An illustration of wavelength and amplitude.

energy. The **amplitude** of a wave is conventionally defined as *half* the trough-to-crest height, or (equivalently) the maximum deviation of the wave from its mean position. Therefore the amplitude of a wave is a measure of how much energy it carries. The meanings of the wavelength and amplitude of a wave are summarized in Figure 8.2.

The preceding discussion of waves in terms of natural water waves on the sea has been rather qualitative. The problem is that waves on the sea are a rather uncontrollable phenomenon: they are not generally well behaved and regular, they are not strictly periodic, and one wave crest breaking on a beach is often quite different in nature to that immediately preceding or following it — just ask a surfer! This makes them difficult to study and therefore waves on the sea are not an ideal subject for examining wave behaviour in general. The goal here is to understand light waves, but unfortunately these are even more difficult to study directly. Of the quantities mentioned above that characterize waves, the wave speed for light is extremely large, and the wavelength, period and amplitude are extremely small. Clearly a more suitable, controlled situation is required which will enable wave behaviour to be examined more closely. In the video 'Making waves', a device known as a *ripple tank* is used to generate uniform, regular waves on the surface of water. These waves *can* be studied in a controlled manner, and the general principles so learned can be applied to wave motion in general. However, before doing Activity 8.1, study Box 8.1, *Inverse proportionality*, which introduces a mathematical concept that will be used in the video.

Box 8.1 *Inverse proportionality*

You have seen a number of examples of proportionality in earlier blocks. For example, the unbalanced force F acting on an object is proportional to the object's acceleration a. This means that when the acceleration doubles, then the unbalanced force must double too. A proportionality relationship may be written as:

$$F \propto a$$

(where the symbol '$\propto$' is read as 'is proportional to'). In Block 5, Box 3.1, we showed that a proportionality can always be converted into an equation by inserting a constant of proportionality k. For instance, the proportionality above can be converted into the equation:

$$F = ka$$

This equation also indicates that if a is doubled, then F is doubled, but if we know the value of k then the equation allows us to calculate a value for F if we know the value of a. Of course, this equation is usually written in the more familiar form $F = ma$, where the symbol m represents the (constant) mass of the object.

There are many situations in which increasing or decreasing one quantity by a certain factor has the *opposite* effect on another quantity. For instance, if you double the speed v at which you travel, you halve the time t taken to complete a journey of a certain distance. If your speed increases by a factor of three, then the time taken decreases by a factor of three. A relationship like this is called an **inverse proportionality**, and it may be written as:

$$t \propto \frac{1}{v}$$

We would say that time t is *inversely proportional to* speed v and you can see from the relationship above that this is equivalent to saying that t is proportional to $\frac{1}{v}$.

An inverse proportionality can be converted into an equation by inserting a constant:

$$t = \frac{k}{v}$$

and in this case the constant of proportionality is the (constant) distance travelled, since $t = \frac{d}{v}$.

Activity 8.1   *Making waves*

In this activity you will watch the video 'Making waves' in which a ripple tank is used to help derive the first crucial equation relating to wave propagation. The video also introduces you to the phenomenon of diffraction and provides essential background information for the practical work you will carry out later in this block. ◀

As you saw in Activity 8.1, a wave may be characterized by its amplitude A, its wavelength λ, its **frequency** f (or period $T = \dfrac{1}{f}$), and its propagation speed v. The units of frequency can be thought of as 'cycles per second' or simply s^{-1}, and an equivalent unit is the **hertz**, where $1\,Hz = 1\,s^{-1}$. (Remember λ is the Greek letter *lambda* — wavelengths are always represented by this symbol.)

As the first task in Activity 8.1 showed, a wave may be represented graphically either by its profile in space at a particular instant of time, or by its variation with time at a particular point in space. Examples of these two representations are shown in Figure 8.3. The speed of a wave v is related to its frequency and wavelength by the equation:

$$v = f\lambda \tag{8.1}$$

With λ in the SI unit of metres and f in the SI unit of hertz (or s^{-1}), the speed of the wave is expressed in the SI unit of $m\,s^{-1}$. The speed of propagation of light waves is given the special symbol c and is equal to $3.00 \times 10^8\,m\,s^{-1}$ (to three significant figures). So for light, or any other electromagnetic radiation:

$$c = f\lambda \tag{8.2}$$

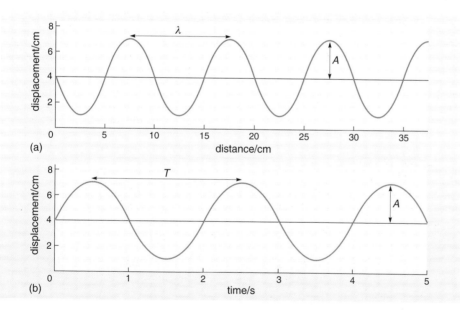

Figure 8.3   The space and time representations of a wave. (a) A graph showing a wave profile at a fixed instant of time, illustrating how the displacement varies with position. The distance between two adjacent positions where the profile has the same displacement, and where the displacement is changing in the same way, is equal to the wavelength λ. (b) A graph showing how the displacement at a fixed point in space varies with time. The interval between two successive times when the displacement is the same, and when the displacement is changing in the same way, is equal to the period T.

The horizontal line at 4 cm represents the mean displacement of the wave.

Question 8.2   Five peaks of a water wave travel past a fixed point in two seconds. (a) What is the period of this wave? (b) What is its frequency? ◀

Question 8.3   Figure 8.3b shows the time representation of a particular wave. Using *only* the information in Figure 8.3b, determine, if possible: (a) the period, (b) the frequency, (c) the amplitude, and (d) the speed of this wave. ◀

Question 8.4   You saw in Activity 8.1 that a red laser beam consists of light that has a *longer* wavelength than that of a green laser beam. What can you say about the relative frequencies of red light and green light? ◀

8.2 The diffraction of light

As you saw in Activity 8.1, **diffraction** is the name given to the process by which waves are 'spread out' by apertures whose size d is similar to the wavelength λ of the wave. A **diffraction pattern** contains places where the waves reinforce each other (diffraction maxima) and places where the waves cancel out (diffraction minima). The spread of a diffraction pattern increases both as the wavelength is *increased*, and as the aperture size is *decreased*.

All waves can be diffracted, and this is a defining property of waves in general.

A **diffraction grating** is a device with many parallel, equally spaced lines ruled on its surface. If a diffraction grating has a spacing of d between adjacent lines, then the number of lines per unit distance is $\dfrac{1}{d}$. When a diffraction grating is illuminated with a laser (which provides a monochromatic source of light), the diffraction pattern produced consists of a series of spots, spaced symmetrically either side of the central position. These spots are referred to as **diffraction orders**, with the one in the centre called the zero order, the pair on either side of it called the first order, the next pair of spots outside those called the second order, and so on. The spread of the spots increases both as the wavelength of the light is *increased*, and as the spacing between the lines of the grating is *decreased*.

As you saw in Activity 8.1, the spread of a diffraction pattern produced by a diffraction grating may be characterized by the distance s_n of the nth spot away from the centre of the pattern. For small values of this distance, s_n is proportional to both the order n and the wavelength λ of the light, but *inversely* proportional to the spacing d between the lines of the grating. The following relationship summarizes this information:

$$s_n \propto \frac{n\lambda}{d}$$

However, as indicated in Activity 8.1, this is only an approximation to the real situation and holds true only when the distances are small. In order to examine the correct relationship between these quantities, some ideas are needed from trigonometry — the study of angles and triangles. These ideas are presented in Box 8.2, *Sines, cosines and tangents*, which you should study now before continuing with this section.

Box 8.2 Sines, cosines and tangents

If necessary, refresh your memory about *angles* and *degrees* by rereading Box 9.1 in Block 2 before studying this box.

Look at the triangle drawn in Figure 8.4a. One angle of this triangle is a *right angle* and is therefore equal to 90°. The side of the triangle facing this is the longest of the three sides and is known as the *hypotenuse*. For convenience, it's labelled *hyp* in the diagram. Another of the angles of the triangle is labelled θ, which is the Greek letter *theta* (pronounced 'thee-ta' where the 'th' is soft as in 'think') and is frequently used to denote angles. The side of the triangle that is opposite the angle θ is labelled accordingly as *opp*, and the side adjacent to the angle is labelled *adj*. A similar triangle can also be drawn, with the same angles as the first triangle, but with the length of each side increased, as shown in Figure 8.4b. The sides of this triangle are labelled with the same abbreviations as the first, but with the symbol ′ ('prime') added.

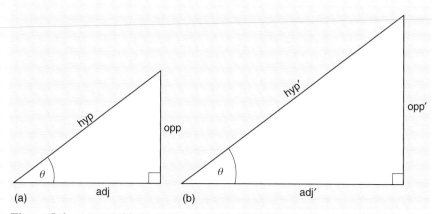

Figure 8.4 (a) and (b) show two triangles of different sizes, but with the same angles as each other. The angle indicated by the symbol □ is known as a right angle and is equal to 90°.

Question 8.5 Each of the angles of the triangle shown in Figure 8.4a is the same size as the corresponding angle of the triangle in Figure 8.4b. Measure the lengths of the sides of these triangles (hyp, opp, adj in Figure 8.4a and hyp′, opp′, adj′ in Figure 8.4b). What are the values of $\left(\dfrac{\text{opp}}{\text{hyp}}\right)$, $\left(\dfrac{\text{adj}}{\text{hyp}}\right)$ and $\left(\dfrac{\text{opp}}{\text{adj}}\right)$ for the triangle in Figure 8.4a? How do these compare with the values $\left(\dfrac{\text{opp}′}{\text{hyp}′}\right)$, $\left(\dfrac{\text{adj}′}{\text{hyp}′}\right)$ and $\left(\dfrac{\text{opp}′}{\text{adj}′}\right)$ for the triangle in Figure 8.4b? ◀

As you saw in Question 8.5, the relative lengths of the sides of a right-angled triangle depend on the angles in that triangle. Turning this argument around, the sizes of the angles in a right-angled triangle depend on the relative lengths of the sides of these triangles. This is such a useful fact that the values you calculated above are given the special names: **sine**, **cosine** and **tangent**, often abbreviated to sin, cos and tan. For the angle θ shown in Figure 8.4a:

$$\sin \theta = \frac{\text{opp}}{\text{hyp}} \tag{8.3a}$$

$$\cos \theta = \frac{\text{adj}}{\text{hyp}} \tag{8.3b}$$

$$\tan \theta = \frac{\text{opp}}{\text{adj}} \tag{8.3c}$$

These three *trigonometric functions*, as they are known, are stored on your calculator. So, for instance, if you key into your calculator: ③ ⓪ SIN or SIN ③ ⓪ depending on its mode of operation, the calculator will display a value of 0.5. Therefore the sine of 30° is 0.5. In any right-angled triangle, in which the length of one side divided by the length of the hypotenuse is 0.5, the angle opposite to the side in question will be 30°. Sine, cosine and tangent functions refer to relative lengths of the sides of a right-angled triangle, and so are independent of the actual size of the triangle, as you saw in Question 8.5, and they have no units.

When you are happy that you understand how to enter sin, cos, and tan on your calculator, try the following exercise to make sure that you are comfortable with these trigonometric functions.

Question 8.6 Use your calculator to find the sine, cosine or tangent of the following angles (quote your answers to two significant figures): (a) sin 60°; (b) cos 60°; (c) tan 60°; (d) cos 30°; (e) cos 45°; (f) sin 45°; (g) sin 10°; (h) cos 10°; (i) tan 10°; (j) tan 80°. ◀

Trigonometry has many uses in the world around us, and Figure 8.5 shows one such example. Here the surveyor measures the angle from the ground to the top of the tower as 60°, and measures her distance from the base of the tower as 20 m. If these values are substituted into Equation 8.3c, it can be used to find the height of the tower:

$$\tan 60° = \frac{\text{height of tower}}{20 \text{ m}}$$

So the height of the tower is equal to 20 m × tan 60° = 35 m (to two significant figures).

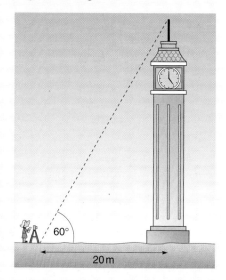

Figure 8.5 Use of trigonometry to measure the height of a tower.

Earlier (in Activity 8.1, Tasks 2 and 3) you quantified the 'spread' of a diffraction pattern by the distance s_n of the nth spot away from the centre of the pattern. As you saw, the distances of the spots did not *quite* increase regularly with n or with $\frac{1}{d}$, but deviated slightly, particularly when the distances s_n were large. There is a good reason for this, namely that the *true* relationship between the wavelength λ and the line spacing of the diffraction grating d depends on the **angle of diffraction** θ_n of the nth order. As you can see in Figure 8.6, the angle of diffraction is defined as the angle between the straight through position and that at which a spot is found in the diffraction pattern.

Figure 8.6 The angle of diffraction θ_n of the nth spot in a diffraction pattern.

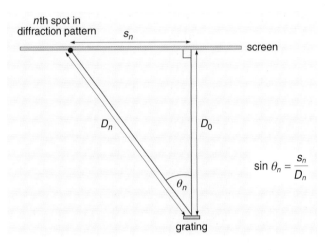

The equation relating the angle of diffraction θ_n to the wavelength λ, grating line spacing d, and order n of the diffraction pattern, is:

$$\sin \theta_n = \frac{n\lambda}{d} \tag{8.4}$$

This equation may be derived from a consideration of the geometry of the situation and an understanding of the propagation behaviour of light waves. However, we will not present the derivation here, since it would be a lengthy detour from the main story. You will shortly see that the equation provides a good explanation for what is observed.

As shown in Figure 8.6, $\sin \theta_n$ is the distance of the nth spot away from the centre of the diffraction pattern divided by the distance from the grating to that spot:

$$\sin \theta_n = \frac{s_n}{D_n}$$

(Remember, the sine of an angle in a right-angled triangle is defined as the length of the side opposite to the angle divided by the length of the longest side of the triangle — see Box 8.2.) So, if we substitute $\frac{s_n}{D_n}$ in place of $\sin \theta_n$, Equation 8.4 can be written as:

$$\frac{s_n}{D_n} = \frac{n\lambda}{d} \tag{8.5}$$

● In Activity 8.1, why were you able to use the proportionality $s_n \propto \frac{n\lambda}{d}$?

When s_n is small, the distance of each spot away from the grating D_n is approximately the same in each case, and roughly equal to D_0, the perpendicular distance between the grating and the screen. In this case the Equation 8.5 becomes

$$\frac{s_n}{D_0} = \frac{n\lambda}{d} \qquad \text{or} \qquad s_n = D_0 \times \frac{n\lambda}{d}$$

Since D_0 is a constant, this may be written as a proportionality: $s_n \propto \dfrac{n\lambda}{d}$.

Using a laser as the source of light, the angles of diffraction θ_n for the various orders of the diffraction pattern can be measured. The line spacing of the grating d can also be measured, using a microscope for instance. In Equation 8.4, the only quantity that cannot be measured directly is λ — the wavelength of the light. Here then is a means of calculating the wavelength of the light used to produce a diffraction pattern. You will do this in Activity 8.2, but before attempting this activity, study Box 8.3, *The equation of a straight line*, which introduces you to a technique you will need to use in this activity.

Box 8.3 *The equation of a straight line*

We showed in Block 3 that if the speed of a seismic wave or a tectonic plate is constant, then the distance travelled by the wave or the plate is proportional to the time taken; so in twice the time a plate will cover twice the distance. We also showed that if we plot a graph of distance travelled versus the time taken, we get a straight line that passes through the origin of the graph. In fact, if values for the two quantities on either side of *any* proportionality relationship (such as $y \propto x$) are plotted against each other on a graph, then the points will lie along a straight line that passes through the origin, as shown in Figure 8.7a.

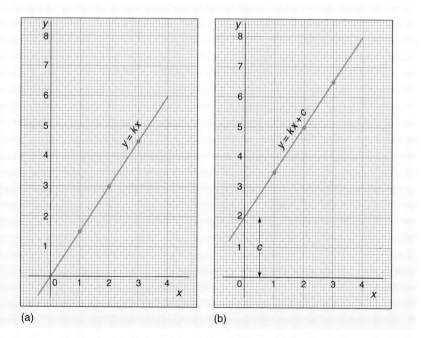

(a)   (b)

Figure 8.7   (a) A graph showing values of a quantity y plotted against corresponding values of x and illustrating the proportionality $y \propto x$. The gradient of this graph is k such that $y = kx$. (b) A graph showing values of a quantity y plotted against corresponding values of x and illustrating the equation $y = kx + c$. The gradient of this graph is k and it intercepts the vertical axis at $y = c$.

Now, we reminded you in Box 8.1 that any proportionality can be converted into an equation by inserting a constant, so $y \propto x$ can be written as:

$$y = kx \qquad (8.6)$$

If we rearrange this equation to make k the subject, then we get

$$k = \frac{y}{x}$$

But we showed in Block 3 that the gradient of a straight line passing through the origin is given by

$$\text{gradient} = \frac{y}{x}$$

Comparing this with the equation $k = \frac{y}{x}$, it is clear that

$$\text{gradient} = k$$

So, if $y = kx$ then a graph of y against x will be a straight line whose gradient is equal to k. Any equation that can be written in the form $y = kx$ is referred to as 'an equation of a straight line'. Notice that when $x = 0$ then $y = 0$, whatever value is taken by k (the gradient of the graph). In other words, when plotted as graphs such equations always correspond to straight lines that pass through the origin.

Now look at the line plotted on the graph in Figure 8.7b. This has the same gradient as the graph in Figure 8.7a, but the whole line has been moved vertically upwards by a distance c. So for

any value of x, we can find the value of y by calculating kx as with the graph in Figure 8.7a, and then adding on an extra amount c corresponding to the vertical shift. So the equation that allows us to calculate a value for y from a value of x is:

$$y = kx + c \qquad (8.7)$$

This is the general form of the **equation of a straight line**.

From this equation you can see that when $x = 0$, then $y = (k \times 0) + c$, and therefore $y = c$. So the value of c indicates the point at which the line intercepts the vertical axis. Such a graph still has a gradient of k, however, as you can see by comparing the gradients of the two graphs in Figure 8.7.

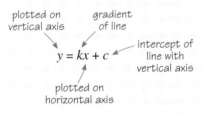

- If c is a negative number, how would the graph differ from that shown in Figure 8.7b?

- The graph would still be a straight line, and would still slope in the same direction, but it would be shifted downwards so that it intercepted the vertical axis in the region where y is negative.

Question 8.7   The gradient of a graph is the 'rise' in y divided by the 'run' in x. Calculate the gradients of the graphs shown in Figures 8.7a and 8.7b, and then write down equations relating y and x in each case that involve numbers in place of k and c. ◀

Question 8.8   The speed of a bus v, measured at a range of times t, is given by the equation $v = u + at$ where u and a are constant values representing the initial speed of the bus and its acceleration, respectively. If you were to plot a graph of speed v on the vertical axis against time t on the horizontal axis, how could you determine the initial speed u and the acceleration a of the bus from the graph? ◀

Question 8.9   The change in the gravitational energy ΔE_g of a locust when it jumps depends on its mass m and the height it reaches above the ground Δh. The equation relating these quantities is $\Delta E_g = mg\Delta h$ where g is the acceleration due to gravity, $9.8~\text{m s}^{-2}$. A graph of ΔE_g plotted against Δh has a gradient of $0.019\,6~\text{kg m s}^{-2}$. What is the mass of the locust? ◀

Activity 8.2   Determining the wavelength of laser light

In this activity you will determine the wavelength of the red laser light using some data from the video 'Making waves' (Activity 8.1).◀

It is convenient to express the wavelengths of visible light in units of nanometres. The prefix **nano** means 10^{-9}, so $1~\text{nm} = 10^{-9}~\text{m}$ and conversely $1~\text{m} = 10^9~\text{nm}$. The wavelength of the red laser light determined in Activity 8.2, $6.36 \times 10^{-7}~\text{m}$, is therefore equivalent to $6.36 \times 10^{-7} \times 10^9~\text{nm}$, or $636~\text{nm}$.

The procedure described in Activity 8.2 is all very well with just a single wavelength of light, such as a laser beam, but what about 'white light' that contains a whole range of wavelengths? As you saw at the end of the 'Making waves' video (Activity 8.1), a diffraction grating effectively spreads out the spectrum of the light source in *each* order of the diffraction pattern, apart from the zero order. The individual orders are spread out into a rainbow of colours, and each colour in the spectrum of the light source appears at a specific position within each order of the diffraction pattern. In this case, Equation 8.4 can be applied as well, but the measurements must always refer to the *same* feature in each order of the spectrum (such as a particular spectral line). You know that the 'blue' lines in each order of the diffraction pattern of the energy saver bulb, for instance, must all correspond to the same wavelength of light — that's what makes them blue! So, if measurements are made of the angles of diffraction for the blue lines in the different orders, the wavelength corresponding to blue light can be calculated. You will do this for yourself in Activity 10.1.

Question 8.10   (a) If a diffraction grating has 500 lines per mm ruled on its surface, how far apart are the individual lines? (Give your answer in μm.)

(b) If the lines on a diffraction grating are 4 μm apart, how many lines per mm are there? ◀

Question 8.11   A laser beam is used to illuminate a diffraction grating (grating A), and the diffraction pattern is projected onto a screen. If grating A is swapped for one which has *more* lines per mm ruled on its surface (grating B), what happens to the spacing of the spots in the diffraction pattern? ◀

Question 8.12   A red laser beam, of wavelength $\lambda = 660$ nm, is used to illuminate a grating with $d = 10$ μm. Many spots are seen on a distant screen, and their positions are marked, as shown in the top row of Figure 8.8.

(a) The grating is now swapped for another, and this time the *first* order spots in the diffraction pattern fall where the *fourth* order spots lay in the original pattern, as shown in the middle row of Figure 8.8. What is the line spacing of the new grating?

(b) The original grating ($d = 10$ μm) is now returned, but the laser is swapped for one producing blue light. Now the *third* order spots lie in the positions originally occupied by the *second* order spots in the diffraction pattern of the red laser beam, as shown in the bottom row of Figure 8.8. What is the wavelength of the blue laser light? ◀

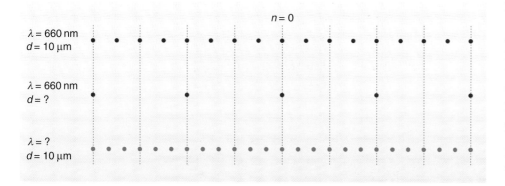

Figure 8.8   For use with Question 8.12. The top row shows the diffraction pattern produced by red light using a diffraction grating with $d = 10$ μm. The middle row shows the diffraction pattern produced by red light, but with a grating of unknown spacing. The bottom row shows the pattern produced by blue light using the original grating with $d = 10$ μm.

8.3 The frequency and wavelength of light

As you have seen, diffraction is one way of determining the wavelength of a wave when it cannot be measured directly. When light is diffracted by a grating, the angles of diffraction of successive orders in the diffraction pattern are determined by just two things: the spacing d of the lines in the grating, and the wavelength of the light. So by using Equation 8.4, $\sin \theta_n = \dfrac{n\lambda}{d}$, and measuring the spacing d, the wavelength of light may be determined. Having determined the wavelength in this way, Equation 8.2, $c = f\lambda$, can then be used to calculate the frequency of the light. We are now in a position to add both frequency and wavelength scales to the electromagnetic spectrum that you saw in Section 2.

The familiar rainbow of colours occupies a very narrow region of the electromagnetic spectrum, with wavelengths in the range from around 4×10^{-7} m (violet) to 7×10^{-7} m (red). The frequencies of these visible limits are about 7.5×10^{14} Hz (violet) and 4.3×10^{14} Hz (red). As shown in Figure 8.9, the wavelength of electromagnetic radiation *decreases* in progressing from radio waves, through microwaves, infrared radiation, light, ultraviolet radiation and X-rays to γ-rays. Conversely, the frequency of electromagnetic radiation *increases* in progressing through the same sequence.

○ Remembering the relationship $c = f\lambda$, are the wavelength and frequency scales in Figure 8.9 consistent with the value of the speed of light ($c = 3 \times 10^8$ m s^{-1})?

○ Yes. For example, the boundary between ultraviolet radiation and X-rays is shown to occur around a frequency of 10^{17} Hz, and a wavelength of 3×10^{-9} m. Multiplying these two numbers gives the speed of light, as required: $(10^{17}\,\text{Hz}) \times (3 \times 10^{-9}\,\text{m}) = 3 \times 10^8\,\text{m s}^{-1}$. (Remember that the unit Hz is equivalent to s^{-1}.)

Figure 8.9 The electromagnetic spectrum showing frequency and wavelength scales, with the visible region of the spectrum shown in expanded form.

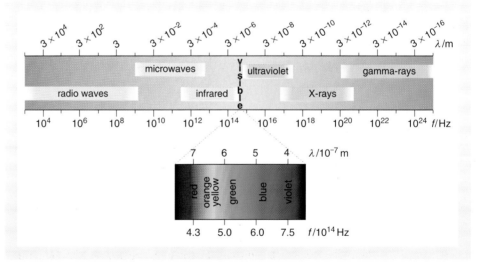

Question 8.13 (a) On the frequency axis of Figure 8.9, mark where 1 kHz, 1 MHz and 1 GHz would occur.

(b) On the wavelength axis, mark where 1 nm, 1 μm and 1 mm would occur. ◀

Question 8.14 A science fiction story mentions a ray-gun that emits a beam with a wavelength of 0.1 nm and a frequency of 100 GHz. Can this beam be any form of electromagnetic radiation? ◀

Question 8.15 (a) As you can see from Figure 8.9, the wavelength of radio waves is from less than a metre to many kilometres — you may know that BBC Radio 4 longwave is broadcast with a wavelength of 1 500 m for instance. Using this wavelength calculate the *frequency* of BBC Radio 4 broadcast on longwave.

(b) FM (frequency modulated) radio broadcasts use the VHF (very high frequency) band. What is the wavelength corresponding to a station broadcasting at a frequency of 100 MHz?

(You should assume that the speed of electromagnetic radiation, $c = 3.00 \times 10^8 \, \text{m s}^{-1}$.) ◀

8.4 Summary of Section 8

The wavelength of a wave is the distance between two neighbouring, similar points on the wave profile, and it is given the symbol λ. The frequency of a wave is the number of cycles of the wave that pass a given point in one second, and it is given the symbol f. The period of a wave T is the time taken for one complete cycle of the wave to pass a fixed point, and is related to its frequency by $T = \dfrac{1}{f}$.

The wavelength and frequency of an electromagnetic wave are related by the equation:

$$c = f\lambda \tag{8.2}$$

where c is the speed of light and has a value of $3.00 \times 10^8 \, \text{m s}^{-1}$ (to three significant figures).

Waves may be diffracted by apertures whose size is similar to the wavelength of the wave. For a diffraction grating with a line spacing d, illuminated with a laser beam of wavelength λ, the diffraction pattern observed on a distant screen consists of a series of spots, known as diffraction orders. The angle of diffraction of the nth order either side of the centre is given by:

$$\sin \theta_n = \frac{n\lambda}{d} \tag{8.4}$$

When a diffraction grating is illuminated by a light source that contains a range of wavelengths, the different wavelengths are effectively spread out in the diffraction pattern. Each order of the diffraction pattern consists of a spectrum of the light source.

Different regions of the electromagnetic spectrum are distinguished by the different wavelengths and frequencies of the radiation. The longest wavelength, lowest frequency, radiation is referred to as radio waves. Moving to shorter wavelengths and higher frequencies the radiation is referred to as microwaves, infrared radiation, light, ultraviolet radiation, and X-rays. The radiation with the shortest wavelength and highest frequency is referred to as γ-rays.

9 Light as particles

Having discussed the wave-like propagation of light and other electromagnetic radiation, it is time to return to a consideration of its particle-like interaction with matter, which you first encountered in Section 2. The discussion will be concerned with *photons*, which, as you've seen, are particles of electromagnetic radiation. In the interaction of light with matter it is the photon's *energy* that is important. So perhaps the first question to address is: How is this energy related to the wave properties of electromagnetic radiation?

The discussion of waves in Section 8.1 noted that waves transport energy from one place to another, and that the amount of energy carried by a wave depends on the wave's amplitude. In the case of sound waves, the energy of the wave manifests itself as the *loudness* of the sound: a louder sound clearly transports more energy than a quieter sound and so must correspond to a wave of larger amplitude. Similarly, it might be expected that the energy of a light wave is related to the *intensity* of the illumination.

Whilst this is true, it is not the end of the story for electromagnetic radiation. Problems with this simple picture for the energy carried by light waves began to become apparent as a result of a series of experiments that were carried out between 1887 and 1902. These experiments, first by Heinrich Hertz, then by J. J. Thomson, and finally Philip Lenard, led to the discovery of a phenomenon known as the photoelectric effect.

9.1 The interaction of electromagnetic radiation and matter

Experiments show that when some metals are illuminated by a strong source of electromagnetic radiation, electrons are emitted from the surface of the metal. This is known as the **photoelectric effect**. Certain metals respond better than others: in particular the alkali metals emit electrons when illuminated with light, whereas for other metals only a source of ultraviolet radiation causes electrons to be emitted. The electrons that are ejected, referred to as **photoelectrons**, do not all emerge with the same kinetic energy, but there is a well-defined maximum kinetic energy that depends on the type of radiation and the type of metal used. The results of the photoelectric effect are illustrated schematically in Figure 9.1 and described in the caption.

These results were perplexing to scientists at the beginning of the 20th century, because they were expecting the light falling on the metal surface to interact as if it were a wave. You have seen already that water waves with a large amplitude impart more kinetic energy to pebbles on a beach than do small ripples. Well, a light wave with a large amplitude corresponds to an intense light, so the scientists expected that high intensity light would eject electrons from a metal with greater kinetic energy than would low intensity light, and they didn't expect that the frequency of the light would have an effect. Yet exactly the opposite was observed to be the case.

Question 9.1   When yellow light is used to illuminate a certain metal, photoelectrons are emitted with a maximum kinetic energy of 0.15 eV.

(a) What can you say about the maximum kinetic energy of the photoelectrons emitted from this metal when it is illuminated with a source of green light?

(b) If a more intense source of yellow light is substituted for the original illumination, what can you say about the maximum kinetic energy of the photoelectrons? ◀

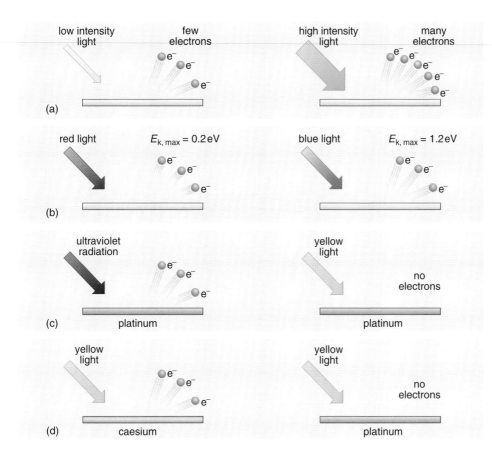

Figure 9.1 The photoelectric effect. (a) Changing the intensity of the radiation. The *number* of photoelectrons emitted by the metal increases as the *intensity* of the radiation is increased, but the range of energies of the photoelectrons remains exactly the same.

(b) Increasing the frequency of the radiation. The higher the *frequency* of the radiation falling on to the metal, the higher the *maximum kinetic energy* of the photoelectrons. In the example shown here, increasing the frequency of the light from red to blue increases the maximum kinetic energy $E_{k,\,max}$ of the photoelectrons from 0.2 eV to 1.2 eV.

(c) Decreasing the frequency of the radiation. There is a lower limit to the frequency of the radiation, below which no photoelectrons are emitted. In the example here, when platinum is illuminated with *ultraviolet radiation*, then photoelectrons are emitted. However, when platinum is illuminated with *yellow light*, then no photoelectrons are emitted, whatever the intensity of the source.

(d) Changing the metal. The lower limit to the frequency is different for different metals. In the example here, when *caesium* is illuminated with yellow light, then photoelectrons are emitted. However, when *platinum* is illuminated with the same source of light, then no photoelectrons are emitted.

9.2 The energy of a photon

As you saw at the beginning of this block, in the year 1900, Max Planck first suggested that light could only interact with matter in discrete quanta with specific amounts of energy. Building on this idea, the first satisfactory explanation for the photoelectric effect was proposed by Albert Einstein in 1905. He argued that a whole quantum of light energy was absorbed by a single electron in the metal. (The quantum of light energy was subsequently named the photon, in 1926, after further experiments revealed that light quanta possessed other particle-like attributes.) Einstein's key idea, expressed in modern terms, was that the energy of a single photon is proportional to the frequency of the light wave that is used to characterize its propagation:

$$E_{ph} = hf \qquad (9.1)$$

This equation states that the energy E_{ph} carried by a photon of light (or any other electromagnetic radiation) is equal to a certain constant h multiplied by the frequency f of the light. The constant represented by the symbol h is the fundamental constant of quantum physics, now known as the **Planck constant**. In Activity 9.1, you will determine for yourself a value for the Planck constant, using the results of an experiment demonstrated in a video.

⬤ What is the SI unit of the Planck constant?

○ The SI unit of energy is the joule, and frequency is measured in hertz, or s^{-1}. Equation 9.1 may be rearranged as $h = \dfrac{E_{ph}}{f}$, so the unit of h can be expressed as joules per hertz ($J\,Hz^{-1}$). However, $1\,Hz = 1\,s^{-1}$, so conversely $1\,Hz^{-1} = 1\,s$. The SI unit for the Planck constant is therefore joule second ($J\,s$).

For our purposes, energies expressed in electronvolts (eV) are often more appropriate, and for this reason, an equally valid unit for the Planck constant is electronvolts per hertz ($eV\,Hz^{-1}$). We shall frequently use this unit for the Planck constant in the rest of this block.

● Bearing in mind Equation 9.1 which relates energy and frequency, and Equation 8.2 which relates frequency and wavelength, what is the expression for the energy of a photon in terms of its wavelength? (Refer back to Box 3.3 in Block 5 if you need to remind yourself how to combine algebraic equations.)

○ Equation 9.1 states that the energy of a photon of electromagnetic radiation is related to its frequency by $E_{ph} = hf$. Equation 8.2 shows that the frequency, wavelength and speed of an electromagnetic wave are related by $c = f\lambda$, where c is the speed of light. In order to substitute for f in Equation 9.1, Equation 8.2 may be rearranged to make f the subject by dividing both sides of the equation by λ, giving $\dfrac{c}{\lambda} = f$. So substituting for f in Equation 9.1 gives:

$$E_{ph} = h \times \frac{c}{\lambda} \qquad \text{or} \qquad E_{ph} = \frac{hc}{\lambda} \qquad\qquad (9.2)$$

Question 9.2 (a) By considering the relative *frequencies* of ultraviolet and infrared radiation (see Figure 8.9), use Equation 9.1 to decide which carries the greater energy: a photon of ultraviolet radiation or a photon of infrared radiation.

(b) By considering the relative *wavelengths* of microwave radiation and light (see Figure 8.9), use Equation 9.2 to decide which carries the greater energy: a photon of microwave radiation or a photon of light. ◀

9.3 Understanding the photoelectric effect

Once Einstein had suggested that light quanta (i.e. photons) carry a discrete amount of energy, with a value related to the frequency of the electromagnetic wave used to characterize its propagation, an explanation of the photoelectric effect was achieved simply by applying the principle of conservation of energy. Einstein proposed that there was a minimum energy E_0 required to release an electron from a metal. He supposed that this value was a constant for a particular metal, but varied from one metal to another. So, when a photon is absorbed by an electron within a metal, two possible outcomes are as follows:

1   If the energy of the photon is less than E_0, then no photoelectron will be emitted, the photon will simply be absorbed, increasing the energy of the metal.

2   If the energy of the photon is greater than E_0 then some of the photon's energy will be 'used up' in freeing the electron from the metal and if there is any energy 'left over' then this will appear as the kinetic energy of the photoelectron that is emitted. In terms of the law of conservation of energy that you met in Block 5:

$$(\text{energy of photon}) = \left(\begin{array}{c}\text{energy needed to} \\ \text{release photoelectron}\end{array}\right) + \left(\begin{array}{c}\text{kinetic energy of} \\ \text{emitted photoelectron}\end{array}\right)$$

The quantum world **Block 7**

This equation is rather like the result for the ionization energy of an atom that you met in Section 2.6. However, as noted in Section 2.7, in a metal, unlike an isolated atom, there is a continuous range of energy levels. So photons with *all* energies can be absorbed, because there will always be a pair of energy levels that are separated by the required energy difference. (For the same reason, a heated metal will emit photons with a continuous range of energies, so giving rise to a continuous spectrum.) Similarly, the range of energies that can release electrons from a metal is also continuous.

Now, when a metal is illuminated with photons of a single energy (and therefore radiation of a single frequency) such that E_{ph} is greater than E_0, then photoelectrons are emitted with a *range* of kinetic energies. Because the energy 'put in' is the same in each case (all the photons have the same energy), we can say that those photoelectrons that emerge with the smallest kinetic energy are the ones that needed the largest amount of energy to free them from the metal, and those photoelectrons that emerge with the largest kinetic energy are those that needed the smallest amount of energy to free them from the metal. The electrons must therefore occupy a variety of quantum states in the metal, with a range of different energies.

According to Einstein's ideas, the *smallest* amount of energy needed to free an electron from the metal is E_0, so the energy conservation equation derived above may be written in symbols as:

$$E_{ph} = E_0 + E_{k,\,max}$$

where $E_{k,\,max}$ is the maximum kinetic energy acquired by any photoelectron. Rearranging this we have the equation, in modern terms, postulated by Einstein as an explanation of the photoelectric effect:

$$E_{k,\,max} = E_{ph} - E_0 \tag{9.3}$$

As noted already, this equation is nothing more than an application of the law of conservation of energy. Now, how do Einstein's ideas explain the observations illustrated in Figure 9.1? Taking each part of the figure in turn:

(a) The fact that the number of photoelectrons increases with the intensity of the light is explained by each photon liberating exactly one photoelectron. A higher intensity of light implies that more photons are present, so more photoelectrons are ejected.

(b) The fact that the maximum kinetic energy of the photoelectrons depends on the frequency of the light is explained because photons corresponding to radiation of a higher frequency carry more energy. So, after energy E_0 has been used by an electron to escape from the metal, there is more energy left over to appear as kinetic energy of the photoelectron.

(c) The fact that there is a lower limit for the frequency of radiation, below which no photoelectrons are emitted, is built into Einstein's assumptions. Since the minimum energy required to eject electrons from a particular metal is E_0, then the minimum frequency radiation needed to do this is $\dfrac{E_0}{h}$.

(d) The fact that the lower limit of frequency is different for different metals arises simply because different metals each have a different value of E_0. In the example shown, caesium has a lower value of E_0 than platinum, and so the lower limit for the frequency of radiation which can eject electrons from its surface is also lower.

Question 9.3   A metal surface is illuminated with photons of blue light, each of which carry an energy of 3.0 eV, and electrons are liberated from the metal.

(a) If one of the photoelectrons has a kinetic energy of 0.7 eV, how much energy was required to remove it from the metal?

(b) If an electron required 2.1 eV to liberate it from the metal, how much kinetic energy does the photoelectron possess? ◀

Activity 9.1   *The photoelectric effect*

This activity involves watching a video of an experiment about the photoelectric effect, and using the data obtained to determine a value for the Planck constant. ◀

In Questions 9.4–9.6 you may assume that the Planck constant $h = 4.1 \times 10^{-15}$ eV Hz^{-1}, and that the speed of light $c = 3.00 \times 10^8$ m s^{-1}.

Question 9.4   An X-ray photon has an energy of 511 keV. What is the corresponding wavelength of this radiation? ◀

Question 9.5   The minimum energy required to eject an electron from a tungsten target is 4.6 eV. What would be the maximum kinetic energy of the photoelectrons produced when ultraviolet radiation of frequency 1.5×10^{15} Hz is shone on a tungsten target? Express your answer in eV. ◀

Question 9.6   Photoelectrons with a maximum kinetic energy of 6.3 eV are emitted from a metal when it is illuminated by ultraviolet radiation with a wavelength of 150 nm.

(a) What is the energy of the incident photons in electronvolts?

(b) What is the wavelength of the radiation corresponding to the lowest energy photons that can free electrons from the metal?

(c) How do you explain the fact that, when infrared radiation is shone on this metal, no photoelectrons are emitted? ◀

9.4   Summary of Section 9

Each photon carries an amount of energy E_{ph} that is determined by the frequency f of the radiation used to characterize its propagation, namely:

$$E_{ph} = hf \tag{9.1}$$

where h is the Planck constant and equal to 4.1×10^{-15} eV Hz^{-1}, or 6.6×10^{-34} J s.

In the photoelectric effect, photons eject electrons from the surfaces of metals. The maximum kinetic energy ($E_{k,\,max}$) of the photoelectrons depends on the frequency of the radiation, but not on its intensity. No electrons are emitted if the photon energy is below a certain minimum value E_0, which varies from one metal to another. From a consideration of the conservation of energy:

$$E_{k,\,max} = E_{ph} - E_0 \tag{9.3}$$

Wave–particle duality

10

We now tie together the two ways of describing light: its wave-like propagation and its particle-like interaction with matter. You will also see that matter can behave both like particles and like waves, given the appropriate conditions.

10.1 Light as waves and particles

You have seen that there are two key equations relating to light and other electromagnetic radiation. The equation that sums up its wave-like propagation is $c = f\lambda$; the equation that sums up its particle-like interaction is $E_{ph} = hf$. As noted earlier, light is neither a wave nor a particle — but in most situations its behaviour can be *described* in terms of one or the other. The words 'wave' and 'particle' bring to mind images of phenomena that are familiar from everyday experience, such as waves on the sea and snooker balls moving around a table. There is really no reason to expect something like electromagnetic radiation to behave in as simple a manner as either of these. It is remarkable, however, that simple wave ideas *can* be used when considering the propagation of electromagnetic radiation, and simple particle ideas *can* be used when considering its interaction with matter.

Activity 10.1 Atomic energy levels

In this activity you will carry out an experiment that relies on both the wave-like propagation and particle-like interaction of light. You will collect your own data and, using the two equations mentioned above, determine for yourself values for the differences between energy levels of atoms. ◀

It is worth pausing for a moment to consider the remarkable experiment that you have just done. Using only a light bulb and a diffraction grating, you have determined values for the differences between energy levels of mercury atoms. Perhaps that seems quite an amazing experiment to be carrying out in your own home! Yet it is based on just a few very simple steps. To summarize what you have done:

1   You measured the angles at which certain spectral lines (different colours) were diffracted by a grating.

2   You then plotted graphs of $\sin \theta_n$ against n for each coloured line, and so determined the wavelength from the gradient using Equation 8.4, $\sin \theta_n = \dfrac{n\lambda}{d}$.

3   Using Equation 8.2, $c = f\lambda$, you converted these wavelengths into frequencies.

4   Using Equation 9.1, $E_{ph} = hf$, you converted these frequencies into photon energies.

5   Finally, using Equation 2.1, $E_{ph} = \Delta E_{atom}$, you equated the energy carried away by the photon with the energy lost by an atom as it changed from one energy level to another.

You are now experienced in dealing with wave–particle duality. You used wave ideas to turn measured angles of diffraction into frequencies; you then used particle ideas to obtain the corresponding energy changes in atoms. This should not be particularly confusing if you bear in mind that each concept has a clearly stated range of applications.

Activity 10.2   Reflections on the practical work

Having just completed the most extensive piece of practical work in the course so far, this activity provides an opportunity to reflect on what you have learned about doing practical work in science. ◀

10.2   Matter as particles and waves

You have seen in the preceding sections that light, which propagates as though it were a wave, interacts as though it is composed of a stream of particles called photons. You may be wondering therefore, whether matter, which is normally thought of as being composed of particles, propagates like a wave. Well, if you are wondering this then congratulate yourself, because 70 years ago, such thoughts could have set you on course for a Nobel prize for physics! The idea that objects such as electrons, which we usually think of as particles, can exhibit wave-like properties was first suggested by Louis de Broglie in 1923 (see Figure 10.1).

This is clearly a very strange concept. After all, light obviously differs from 'matter': the nature of light can be determined only by indirect observations such as diffraction and the photoelectric effect, whereas material objects can usually be seen. You can see that a handful of salt is made of individual grains and in everyday experience salt does not exhibit any wave-like properties. But salt grains are crystals of sodium chloride, these in turn are composed of atoms of sodium and chlorine, which in turn are composed of electrons, protons and neutrons, and the nucleons are composed of quarks — none of which can be seen directly any more than light waves or photons can. When talking about wave-like behaviour of particles, it is these smallest components that are relevant.

If particles, such as electrons, propagate as though they are waves, they should exhibit wave-like behaviour. The crucial property that demonstrates wave-like behaviour is diffraction. So, can a beam of electrons be diffracted? Well, yes it can, providing an object is used that has a sufficiently small 'gap' for the electrons to be diffracted through. The gaps in ordinary diffraction gratings are simply too large to cause any noticeable diffraction to occur with a beam of electrons. However, a beam of electrons may be diffracted using many substances that possess a 'crystal' structure — that is the atoms of which they are composed lie in regularly spaced planes. The spacing between these planes has a somewhat similar effect to the slits in a diffraction grating, but the planes have a spacing that is much smaller — typically a few nanometres.

Remember what was said earlier about the conditions necessary for diffraction to occur: the apertures must be of similar size to the wavelength of the waves concerned. This implies that the wavelength of a beam of electrons is typically less than a nanometre if it is to be diffracted by a crystal. The wavelength of an electron beam is determined by the energy that the electrons possess.

⬤ What type of electromagnetic radiation would you expect to be diffracted by apertures whose size is a few nanometres?

◯ X-rays have wavelengths of around a nanometre (see Figure 8.9), so they should also be diffracted by the same structures that diffract electrons.

This is illustrated in Figure 10.2 which shows examples of X-ray and electron diffraction patterns.

Figure 10.1   Prince Louis Victor de Broglie (1892–1987) was the first person to propose that particles can, in some circumstances, behave as waves. He was influenced by Einstein's work on the photoelectric effect, and in 1923 suggested that particles, such as electrons, might behave as waves, and could be diffracted. Not many of his colleagues took these ideas seriously, but Einstein enthusiastically advocated that they be tested experimentally. Within four years, electron diffraction patterns had been produced, so proving de Broglie to be correct.

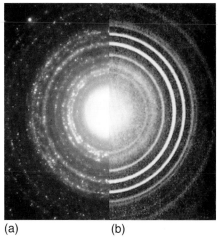

Figure 10.2 Photographs of diffraction patterns obtained with a target made of zirconium oxide: (a) using a beam of electrons and (b) using X-rays (electro-magnetic radiation). The wavelength of the electron beam was set to be the same as the wavelength of X-rays. Because the zirconium and oxygen atoms in the crystal form a three-dimensional structure, the diffraction pattern is more complex than those produced using simple (one-dimensional) diffraction gratings that you saw earlier.

(a)   (b)

But, you may be wondering, why can't diffraction effects be detected with everyday objects? The reason is that massive objects have a large amount of energy, and the larger the energy of an object, the smaller its wavelength. For this reason, you are not noticeably diffracted when you walk through a doorway — your wavelength is simply too small compared with the width of the doorway.

Question 10.1   The inside of the screen in a television set has a coating that emits light when electrons strike it. (This is how TV pictures are produced.) Imagine that you have such a screen, and a special diffraction grating whose lines are only a few nanometres apart.

(a) If a beam of electrons, all of which have the same energy, is fired at this grating, as shown in Figure 10.3, describe what you would see on the screen.

(b) How would the diffraction pattern alter if electrons with a range of energies were used? ◀

10.3 Summary of Section 10

Light always propagates like a wave and always interacts like a beam of particles, called photons. In truth it is neither a wave nor a particle, but it is convenient to describe its behaviour in terms of one or the other, as the situation dictates.

Just as electromagnetic radiation interacts with matter as though it were a stream of particles, so electrons propagate as though they were a wave. This is illustrated by the fact that a beam of electrons can be diffracted by the closely packed planes of atoms in a crystal. The wavelength of a beam of electrons is typically less than 1 nm and decreases as the electron energy is increased.

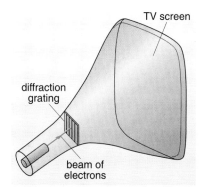

Figure 10.3 The arrangement of electron beam, diffraction grating and TV screen described in Question 10.1.

11 The world taken apart

You have now completed the first half of the course and have reached the end point of our quest to 'take the world apart'. The final stages of this journey, covered in Blocks 6 and 7, have revealed that all material objects are composed of atoms, which in turn consist of negatively charged electrons surrounding a positively charged nucleus. The nuclei of atoms are made up of protons and neutrons, which in turn are formed from combinations of up and down quarks. So to build everything around us (except for a few exotic particles glimpsed in particle accelerators) requires only three types of particle: electrons, up quarks and down quarks. Ghostly particles known as electron neutrinos complete the picture of the material world.

Our understanding of these fundamental building blocks is based on quantum physics. This tells us that we can have no absolute knowledge of the position of an individual particle, or the speed with which it moves. All we can ever hope to measure is some kind of probability for finding it in a certain place at a certain time. Particles that are bound together — such as electrons and nuclei in atoms — do have a well-defined energy, however. So well-defined in fact, that the energy of an atom is only allowed to have certain specific values. Between these allowed energy levels, dramatic quantum jumps occur.

It is these jumps that provide the link with the other important component of the world around us: electromagnetic radiation. When an atom jumps from one energy level to another, such that it loses energy, a photon is emitted whose energy corresponds exactly to the energy difference between the two energy levels. Alternatively, a photon whose energy corresponds exactly to the energy difference between two energy levels of an atom may be absorbed, so raising the energy of the atom and exciting it to the higher energy level.

Light is just one example of electromagnetic radiation. It describes photons that have energies of a few electronvolts. Photons with more energy are described as ultraviolet radiation, X-rays or γ-rays. Photons with less energy are referred to as infrared radiation, microwaves, or radio waves. And these names remind us of another aspect of the quantum world: electromagnetic radiation propagates as though it is a wave, even though it interacts with matter as though it is composed of particles.

Like all waves, electromagnetic radiation is diffracted by apertures which are of a size comparable to the wavelength of the wave involved. This phenomenon provides evidence for a final quantum aspect of nature. Things which we usually think of as particles, such as electrons, can also be diffracted. So they too travel from place to place as though they are a wave. This wave–particle duality lies at the heart of our quantum world.

We hope you have found that your journey in search of the fundamental components of the world around you has been intriguing and challenging. In the second half of the course we will 'put the world together' in an attempt to understand the behaviour of more complex systems.

Activity 11.1   Reviewing your study of Block 7: dealing with difficult material

In this activity you will reflect on your study of Block 7, especially any areas which you found hard. ◀

Questions: answers and comments

Question 1.1   A quantum of light is a very small amount of energy by everyday standards. So it is not normally apparent that light is emitted and absorbed in multiples of this small quantity.

Question 2.1   The absorption spectrum in Figure 2.5 contains absorption lines at *precisely* the same locations (i.e. the same colours) as the emission lines that are seen in the hydrogen spectrum in Figure 2.4. Since the two spectra have the same 'spectral fingerprint', the unknown vapour must be hydrogen. {Note that the 'spectral fingerprint' can be either an emission or an absorption spectrum and this question shows how the two are related.}

Question 2.2   Since $1\,\text{eV} = 1.6 \times 10^{-19}\,\text{J}$, then $1\,\text{J} = \dfrac{1\,\text{eV}}{1.6 \times 10^{-19}}$. So the energy of quanta of green light,

$$3.8 \times 10^{-19}\,\text{J} = 3.8 \times 10^{-19} \times \frac{1\,\text{eV}}{1.6 \times 10^{-19}}$$
$$= 2.4\,\text{eV}$$

{In general, to convert from joules to electronvolts we need to multiply by $\dfrac{1\,\text{eV}}{1.6 \times 10^{-19}\,\text{J}}$. Conversely, to convert from electronvolts to joules we multiply by $\dfrac{1.6 \times 10^{-19}\,\text{J}}{1\,\text{eV}}$.}

Question 2.3   (a) From Figure 2.8, you can see that the energy of each photon of microwave radiation is around 10^{-21} to $10^{-25}\,\text{J}$.

(b) From Figure 2.8, you can see that the energy of each X-ray photon is around 10^{2} to $10^{6}\,\text{eV}$, or about 0.1 keV to 1 MeV.

Question 2.4   The values for the five spectral lines in the visible part of the hydrogen spectrum are about: 1.9 eV (red), 2.6 eV (blue-green), 2.9 eV (deep blue), 3.0 eV (violet) and 3.1 eV (also violet). {You were asked to estimate the values, so your values may differ slightly from these. Don't forget that there are spectral lines in other parts of the electromagnetic spectrum too.}

Question 2.5   (a) If a helium atom absorbs a photon of energy 2.11 eV, then the energy of the atom must *increase* by exactly this amount.

(b) If a mercury atom emits a photon of energy 2.27 eV, then the energy of the atom must *decrease* by exactly this amount.

Question 2.6   Using Equation 2.1, the photon energy is equal to the change in energy of the atom ΔE_{atom}, which is the higher energy level minus the lower energy level, so in this case the photon energy, $E_{\text{ph}} = E_{\text{hi}} - E_{\text{lo}}$.

Question 2.7   (a) The energy of the photon is given by the difference between the two energies, in this case $E_4 - E_3$. Since the final energy (E_4) is higher than the initial energy (E_3) in this case, the photon would have to be absorbed.

(b) In this case the final energy is less than the initial energy, so a photon of energy $E_2 - E_1$ is emitted.

(c) Figure 2.10 shows that the transition from E_7 to E_1 corresponds to an energy difference which is substantially more than that involved in the transition from E_7 to E_2. But the transition between E_7 and E_2 corresponds to an energy difference of 3.12 eV which is near the *upper* energy limit of the visible spectrum (Figure 2.6). The photon associated with the E_7 to E_1 transition is therefore not in the visible part of the spectrum. {In fact this transition corresponds to a photon of ultraviolet radiation.}

(d) Figure 2.10 shows that the transition from E_5 to E_6 corresponds to an energy difference which is substantially less than that involved in the transition from E_2 to E_3, for instance. But the transition between E_2 and E_3 corresponds to an energy difference of 1.89 eV which is near the *lower* energy limit of the visible spectrum (Figure 2.6). The photon associated with the E_5 to E_6 transition is therefore not in the visible part of the spectrum. {In fact this transition corresponds to a photon of infrared radiation.}

Question 2.8   You cannot deduce the values of the energies corresponding to the energy levels of helium, but you can say something about the *separation* of the levels. Because there are three bright spectral lines there must be at least four levels, and pairs of these levels must be separated by the energies of the emitted photons, i.e. 1.76 eV, 2.11 eV and 2.77 eV.

{However, several different possibilities exist, some of which are shown in Figure 2.14. To decide just which (if any) of these is the correct pattern of energy levels would require that further lines be identified. More will be said about the helium spectrum and the corresponding energy levels of helium atoms in Section 4.}

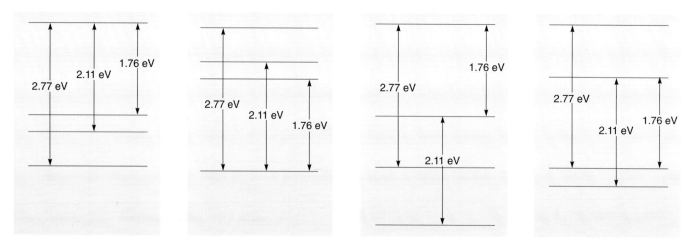

Figure 2.14 A few possible arrangements for the separation of some of the energy levels of helium, deduced in the answer to Question 2.8.

Question 2.9 (a) For $n = 1$, the energy is

$$E_1 = \frac{-13.60\,\text{eV}}{1^2} = -13.60\,\text{eV}$$ which agrees with Figure

2.11. As n becomes larger and larger, $\frac{-13.60\,\text{eV}}{n^2}$

approaches zero ever more closely, so $E_\infty = 0\,\text{eV}$, which again agrees with Figure 2.11. {You can't really talk about putting n 'equal to infinity' since infinity is not a number. It's bigger than any number you can think of, so all you can do is consider what happens as n *approaches infinity*.}

(b) According to the formula:

$$E_{10} = \frac{-13.60\,\text{eV}}{10^2} = \frac{-13.60\,\text{eV}}{100}$$
$$= -0.136\,\text{eV}$$

$$E_{100} = \frac{-13.60\,\text{eV}}{100^2} = \frac{-13.60\,\text{eV}}{10^4}$$
$$= -1.36 \times 10^{-3}\,\text{eV}$$

(c) The photon would have energy:

$$E_{11} - E_{10} = \left(\frac{-13.60\,\text{eV}}{11^2}\right) - \left(\frac{-13.60\,\text{eV}}{10^2}\right)$$
$$= -0.1124\,\text{eV} + 0.1360\,\text{eV}$$
$$= 0.0236\,\text{eV} = 2.36 \times 10^{-2}\,\text{eV}$$

Since the initial level ($n = 10$) is lower than the final level ($n = 11$) the photon would be absorbed.

Question 2.10 The five visible lines in the spectrum of atomic hydrogen correspond to the transitions E_3 to E_2, E_4 to E_2, E_5 to E_2, E_6 to E_2 and E_7 to E_2. These are all in the Balmer series. {Note that not all the Balmer lines are visible: the transitions to E_2 from E_8 and energy levels above this are all in the ultraviolet part of the electromagnetic spectrum.}

Question 2.11 (a) The lines of the Lyman series all correspond to transitions down to the $n = 1$ energy level of hydrogen. Using the values for the energy levels from Figure 2.11, the first five lines will have the following energies:

$$E_2 - E_1 = (-3.40\,\text{eV}) - (-13.60\,\text{eV}) = 10.20\,\text{eV}$$

$$E_3 - E_1 = (-1.51\,\text{eV}) - (-13.60\,\text{eV}) = 12.09\,\text{eV}$$

$$E_4 - E_1 = (-0.85\,\text{eV}) - (-13.60\,\text{eV}) = 12.75\,\text{eV}$$

$$E_5 - E_1 = (-0.54\,\text{eV}) - (-13.60\,\text{eV}) = 13.06\,\text{eV}$$

$$E_6 - E_1 = (-0.38\,\text{eV}) - (-13.60\,\text{eV}) = 13.22\,\text{eV}$$

(b) The photons corresponding to the highest energy line in the Lyman series will have energy:

$$E_\infty - E_1 = (0\,\text{eV}) - (-13.60\,\text{eV}) = 13.60\,\text{eV}$$

(c) Since these energies are all greater than 3.2 eV (the upper limit for visible radiation), these lines will all lie in the ultraviolet part of the electromagnetic spectrum.

(d) If they were equally 'bright' the lines of the Lyman series would form a 'bunched' pattern of the kind shown in Figure 2.15.

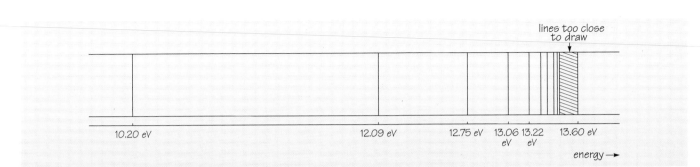

lines too close
to draw

10.20 eV   12.09 eV   12.75 eV   13.06 13.22   13.60 eV
                                            eV   eV

energy →

Figure 2.15 Answer to Question 2.11d. The Lyman series of the hydrogen spectrum.

Question 2.12 (a) The spectrum produced by a glowing copper wire would be a continuous spectrum for the reasons outlined in Section 2.7. The spectrum would contain visible and infrared radiation, spread over a whole range of energies.

(b) The spectrum produced by a vapour of copper atoms that are excited by an electric current would be an emission spectrum, such as those shown in Figure 2.4. The spectrum would contain radiation at certain discrete energies, that is it would contain spectral lines, and these lines would appear in the infrared, visible and ultraviolet regions of the spectrum.

Question 3.1 (a) If the hydrogen atom is isolated from other sources of energy, then it cannot jump from its ground state to an excited state. Also, there is no lower energy level to which the atom could jump, so the statement is correct.

(b) The second energy level has an energy of
$$E_2 = \frac{-13.60\,\text{eV}}{2^2} = -3.40\,\text{eV}$$
(as shown on Figure 2.11). So a photon energy of $(-3.40\,\text{eV}) - (-13.60\,\text{eV}) = 10.20\,\text{eV}$ is needed to excite the atom to the second energy level. If each photon has less than 10 eV of energy there is no way any of them can excite a hydrogen atom from its ground state, so this statement too is correct.

(c) If a hydrogen atom in its ground state absorbs a photon of energy 12.75 eV it will make a transition to an excited state with an energy of $(-13.60\,\text{eV}) + (12.75\,\text{eV}) = -0.85\,\text{eV}$. This is the E_4 energy level, since
$$E_4 = \frac{-13.60\,\text{eV}}{4^2} = -0.85\,\text{eV}$$
(as shown on Figure 2.11). From here the atom can make transitions to *any* of the lower energy levels. Only those transitions ending up at the E_2 energy level will involve emission of visible photons (see Section 2.6). Other

transitions, to the E_3 or E_1 levels, will result in the emission of infrared or ultraviolet photons, respectively. So although the atom *could* emit a visible photon, we cannot say that it definitely *will* do so. Once again, therefore, this statement is correct.

Question 3.2 According to the Bohr model, when a hydrogen atom makes a transition between the energy level E_3 and the ground state, the electron makes a transition from the $n = 3$ orbit to the $n = 1$ orbit. Initially, then, the atom has energy
$$E_3 = \frac{-13.60\,\text{eV}}{3^2} = -1.51\,\text{eV}$$
and radius $r_3 = 3^2 \times 5.29 \times 10^{-11}\,\text{m} = 4.76 \times 10^{-10}\,\text{m}$. When the electron has made the transition, the atom is in the ground state, where it has energy
$$E_1 = \frac{-13.60\,\text{eV}}{1^2} = -13.60\,\text{eV}$$
and radius $r_1 = 1^2 \times 5.29 \times 10^{-11}\,\text{m} = 5.29 \times 10^{-11}\,\text{m}$.

The energy of the atom therefore decreases and this energy is transferred to the photon that is emitted. The energy of the emitted photon is, therefore, $E_3 - E_1 = (-1.51\,\text{eV}) - (-13.60\,\text{eV}) = 12.09\,\text{eV}$.

Question 3.3 As shown in Figure 2.12, Balmer emission lines correspond to transitions to the $n = 2$ energy level from the higher energy levels, $n = 3, 4, 5$, etc. So, according to the Bohr model, in these particular transitions, the electron moves to the second closest orbit to the nucleus from the other orbits that are further away, and in doing so emits photons of energies corresponding to the spectral lines in the Balmer series.

Question 3.4 According to the Bohr model, when the hydrogen atom is in its ground state, the electron will always be found at the same fixed distance from the nucleus, namely $5.29 \times 10^{-11}\,\text{m}$. According to the Schrödinger model, the electron may be found at any distance from the nucleus: the model predicts only the probability of finding the electron within any given range of distance from the nucleus. The most probable distance from the nucleus at which the electron will be found is 5.29×10^{-11} m.

Question 3.5 For $n = 3$, the allowed values of l are $l = 0$, $l = 1$, and $l = 2$. The number of states with each value of l is given by $2 \times (2l + 1)$, so there are $2 \times (2 \times 0 + 1) = 2$ states with $l = 0$, there are $2 \times (2 \times 1 + 1) = 6$ states with $l = 1$, and $2 \times (2 \times 2 + 1) = 10$ states with $l = 2$. The total number of possibilities is, therefore, $2 + 6 + 10 = 18$, and this is equal to $2n^2$.

Question 3.6 (a) The answer does not depend on the fact that $n = 4$, provided that the l value is allowed by $l < n$, which is the case for 4s, 4p, 4d and 4f states, with $l = 0, 1, 2, 3$. Using the $2 \times (2l + 1)$ rule, the numbers of states in each case are 2, 6, 10, 14.

(b) The energies of these states are all given by Equation 3.1 as

$$E_4 = \frac{-13.60 \text{ eV}}{4^2} = -0.85 \text{ eV}$$

(c) A check that all the $n = 4$ states are accounted for is provided by the fact that $2 + 6 + 10 + 14 = 32$; this agrees with the $2n^2$ rule because, for $n = 4$, $2n^2 = 2 \times 4^2 = 32$.

Question 3.7 The ring is white because the probability of finding an electron within it is comparatively low: around this distance from the nucleus, you are much less likely to detect the electron than at smaller distances, or at somewhat larger distances.

Question 3.8 The electron is always detected as a particle, so it can't be in two places at once. The lobes indicate that there are equal chances of finding the electron in either location when a measurement of its position is made. However, any single measurement will find the electron in one of the lobes: we never find half an electron in one lobe and half in the other lobe.

Question 3.9 (a) This is not correct as it is too vague. The Heisenberg uncertainty principle says that if you know the position of a particle precisely, then there's a large uncertainty in its velocity, but there is nothing in the principle that prevents a precise measurement of position.

(b) This is correct (it is mentioned in the text).

(c) This is not correct. The Heisenberg uncertainty principle asserts that the indeterminacies are unavoidable

as they are inherent in the nature of the Universe. The existence of such limitations on our knowledge is just 'the way things are'.

(d) This is certainly not correct. Because the limitations of his principle are an unavoidable aspect of the nature of the Universe, experimenters cannot possibly be expected to overcome them. All that can be asked of experimenters is to minimize the uncertainties of their measurements within the limits set by the uncertainty principle.

Question 4.1 (a) For a Be^{3+} ion, the nuclear charge $Z = 4$, so the ground-state energy may be calculated from Equation 4.1 as:

$$E_1 = 4^2 \times \left(\frac{-13.60 \text{ eV}}{1^2} \right)$$
$$= 16 \times (-13.60 \text{ eV}) = -217.6 \text{ eV}$$

(b) The energy levels of Be^{3+} are like those of H, He^+ and Li^{2+}, all of which contain a single bound electron. The energy of the first excited state of the Be^{3+} ion may be found by setting $Z = 4$ and $n = 2$ in Equation 4.1. In this case we get

$$E_2 = 4^2 \times \left(\frac{-13.60 \text{ eV}}{2^2} \right) = -54.40 \text{ eV}$$

This is the same result as with $Z = 2$ and $n = 1$, corresponding to the ground state of the He^+ ion, namely

$$E_1 = 2^2 \times \left(\frac{-13.60 \text{ eV}}{1^2} \right) = -54.40 \text{ eV}$$

Question 4.2 (a) Setting $Z = 3$ in Equation 4.3, we get $Z_{est} = 3 - 0.3125 = 2.6875$. So, using Equation 4.2, an estimate for the ground-state energy of Li^+ is

$$E_{est} = 2 \times (2.6875)^2 \times (-13.60 \text{ eV}) = -196.5 \text{ eV}$$

(b) Setting $Z = 3$ and $n = 1$ in Equation 4.1, we get

$$E_1 = 3^2 \times \left(\frac{-13.60 \text{ eV}}{1^2} \right) = -122.4 \text{ eV}$$

for the ground-state energy of Li^{2+}. {So it requires 122.4 eV to remove the remaining electron from a Li^{2+} ion.}

(c) The energy that must be supplied to a Li^+ ion in order to remove one more electron and turn it into a Li^{2+} ion is therefore $E_{ionization} = (-122.4 \text{ eV}) - (-196.5 \text{ eV}) = 74.1 \text{ eV}$. So the estimate is that about 74.1 eV must be supplied to the Li^+ ion in order to ionize it further to Li^{2+}. This is illustrated in Figure 4.4.

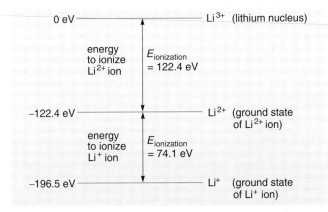

Figure 4.4 Part of the energy-level diagram for lithium ions.

Question 4.3 (a) Since each s state can accommodate two electrons, the ground-state electron configuration for beryllium is $1s^2 2s^2$.

(b) Since the fifth electron cannot go into either the 1s state or the 2s state, which are filled with four electrons, the ground-state electron configuration for boron is $1s^2 2s^2 2p^1$.

(c) The 1s, 2s and 2p sub-shells can accommodate a total of $2 + 2 + 6 = 10$ electrons. {This corresponds to the ground state of the neon atom, $1s^2 2s^2 2p^6$.}

Question 5.1 Since there are four more α-decays, the total decrease in mass number is $(4 \times 4) = 16$, and the total decrease in atomic number is $(4 \times 2) = 8$. So the resultant nucleus has $A = 230 - 16 = 214$ and $Z = 90 - 8 = 82$. The element with atomic number 82 is lead, as noted in the question, so the resulting nucleus is the lead isotope $^{214}_{82}\text{Pb}$.

Question 5.2 (a) Since the decrease in mass is $4.87 \, \text{MeV}/c^2$, the energy liberated by the decay is simply $4.87 \, \text{MeV}$.

(b) Since $5.15 \, \text{MeV}$ of energy is liberated by the decay, the mass of the products must be $5.15 \, \text{MeV}/c^2$ less than that of the original nucleus.

Question 5.3 The nitrogen isotope will undergo β^--decay as follows:

$$^{16}_{7}\text{N} \longrightarrow \, ^{16}_{8}\text{O} + e^- + \overline{\nu}_e$$

Since the resulting nucleus has an atomic number of eight, this is an isotope of oxygen (see Block 6 Study File, Appendix). {Note that the atomic number Z *increases* by one, and the mass number A remains unchanged, and this is true for *all* β^--decays, whatever the initial nucleus.}

Question 5.4 The phosphorus isotope will undergo β^+-decay as follows:

$$^{30}_{15}\text{P} \longrightarrow \, ^{30}_{14}\text{Si} + e^+ + \nu_e$$

Since the resulting nucleus has an atomic number of 14, this is an isotope of silicon (see Block 6 Study File, Appendix). {Note that the atomic number Z *decreases* by one, and the mass number A remains unchanged, and this is true for *all* β^+-decays, whatever the initial nucleus. Compare this with the β^--decay shown in the answer to Question 5.3.}

Question 5.5 β^-- and β^+-decay are clearly rather similar processes. In β^--decay, a neutron transforms into a proton with the emission of an electron and an electron antineutrino; in β^+-decay a proton transforms into a neutron with the emission of a positron and an electron neutrino. So two particles are emitted in each case, one a matter particle and the other an antimatter particle. In β^--decay, the atomic number *increases* by one, and in β^+-decay it *decreases* by one. In both types of decay, the mass number of the nucleus remains unchanged and charge is conserved.

Question 5.6 In the process of γ-decay, the number of protons and neutrons in the nucleus remains unchanged. So the atomic number and mass number of the barium nucleus after the γ-decay are the same as they were before, namely 56 and 137, respectively.

Question 6.1 Since the neutron has charge $Q = 0$ and is composed of three up or down quarks, its quark content must be (udd), giving a charge $Q = +\frac{2}{3}e - \frac{1}{3}e - \frac{1}{3}e = 0$.

Question 6.2 (a) You have seen that the quark content of a proton is (uud), so the antiquark content of an antiproton must be $(\overline{u}\overline{u}\overline{d})$. Now, the charge of an antiquark is opposite to that of the corresponding quark. So the charge of a $\overline{u}$ antiquark is $-\frac{2}{3}e$ whilst the charge of a $\overline{d}$ antiquark is $+\frac{1}{3}e$. The charge of an antiproton is therefore $-\frac{2}{3}e - \frac{2}{3}e + \frac{1}{3}e = -e$. This is the opposite charge to that of a proton, as expected.

(b) Similarly, you have seen that the quark content of a neutron is (udd), so the antiquark content of an antineutron must be $(\overline{u}\overline{d}\overline{d})$. Using the values for the charge of a $\overline{u}$ antiquark and a $\overline{d}$ antiquark from above, the charge of an antineutron is therefore $-\frac{2}{3}e + \frac{1}{3}e + \frac{1}{3}e = 0$. Notice that this is the *same* as the charge of a neutron, even though the antineutron is composed of antiquarks.

Question 6.3   To get a negative charge for π^- we need the combination $(d\,\bar{u})$, with charge $Q = -\frac{1}{3}e - \frac{2}{3}e = -e$.

Question 6.4   Pions and nucleons contain only up and down quarks, so these are the only 'raw materials' available from which to build the new hadron. To get a charge of $+2e$ requires three up quarks $(+\frac{2}{3}e + \frac{2}{3}e + \frac{2}{3}e = +2e)$. This hadron can be formed by the collision of a π^+, $(u\bar{d})$, with a proton, (uud), followed by the annihilation of $\bar{d}$ with d. Since the hadron contains three quarks, it is a baryon.

Question 7.1   (a) Figure 2.2b showed that the spectrum of light from a sodium lamp is an emission spectrum with light at only a single energy. In fact this energy is $E_{ph} = 2.1$ eV. So the spectral distribution, shown in Figure 7.3a has a large 'spike' at this energy.

(b) The continuous spectrum of light from the tungsten filament lamp will be absorbed by the atoms of the sodium vapour. However, absorption will only occur at certain specific energies. In the visible part of the spectrum, this occurs at only a single energy, as shown in Figure 2.2c. The resulting spectral distribution, shown in Figure 7.3b is that of an absorption spectrum, with absorption at an energy $E_{ph} = 2.1$ eV.

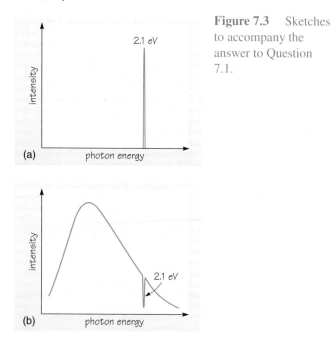

Figure 7.3   Sketches to accompany the answer to Question 7.1.

Question 8.1   (a) If the wave crests are further apart then, as long as the wave is travelling at the same speed as before, a longer time interval will elapse between each crest breaking on the beach and the next. The period of the wave is therefore longer.

(b) If the waves are travelling more quickly across the sea, but with the wave crests the same distance apart as before, then there will be a shorter time interval between each crest breaking on the beach and the next. The period of the wave will therefore be shorter.

Question 8.2   (a) If five peaks travel past a fixed point in two seconds, then the time interval between one peak and the next is $\frac{2\text{ s}}{5} = 0.4$ seconds. The period of the wave is therefore $T = 0.4$ s.

(b) The frequency of the wave can be thought of as simply the number of peaks that pass a fixed point in one second. In this case, five peaks pass a fixed point in two seconds, so two and a half peaks pass by in one second. Alternatively, you can see that, since $f = \frac{1}{T}$, then $f = \frac{1}{0.4\text{ s}} = 2.5$ s^{-1} or 2.5 Hz.

Question 8.3   (a) The period of a wave is the time interval between successive instants when similar parts of the wave profile pass a particular point. Since Figure 8.3b shows the behaviour of a wave over *time* at a particular point in *space*, the period of the wave can be measured as the time between successive peaks, or successive troughs, of the wave, for instance. In Figure 8.3b, the peaks of the wave occur at times $t = 0.5$ s, $t = 2.5$ s and $t = 4.5$ s. Hence the period of the wave is $T = 2.0$ s.

(b) The frequency of the wave is defined as $f = \frac{1}{T}$, so $f = \frac{1}{2.0\text{ s}} = 0.50$ Hz.

(c) The amplitude A of a wave is defined as the maximum displacement of the wave above and below its mean value, or *half* the peak-to-trough height. From Figure 8.3b, the amplitude of the wave is 3.0 cm.

(d) Using only Figure 8.3b it is impossible to determine the speed of propagation of this wave.

{In order to calculate the speed you would need to know the wavelength as well as the frequency. Such information is contained in Figure 8.3a. If these two figures illustrate the *same* wave, then the *combined* information from the two graphs is sufficient to specify the wave completely. Figure 8.3b yields the period, $T = 2.0$ s (and frequency, $f = 0.50$ Hz) and Figure 8.3a yields the wavelength, $\lambda = 10.0$ cm. These two values then enable the wave speed to be calculated, using Equation 8.1, $v = f\lambda = (0.50\text{ Hz}) \times (10.0\text{ cm}) = 5.0$ cm s^{-1}.}

Question 8.4   All light, whether red, green or any other colour, travels at the same speed, $c = 3.00 \times 10^8 \, \text{m s}^{-1}$. So, since Equation 8.2 indicates that the wavelength and frequency of a light wave are related by $c = f\lambda$, multiplying the frequency and wavelength for red light must give the same value as multiplying the frequency and wavelength for green light. Therefore, if red light has a *longer* wavelength than green light, then red light must also have a *smaller* frequency than green light.

Question 8.5   The lengths of the sides of the triangles in Figures 8.4a and 8.4b are: opp = 3.0 cm, adj = 4.0 cm, hyp = 5.0 cm, opp′ = 4.5 cm, adj′ = 6.0 cm, and hyp′ = 7.5 cm. The values calculated for the smaller triangle are $\dfrac{\text{opp}}{\text{hyp}} = \dfrac{3.0}{5.0} = 0.6$, $\dfrac{\text{adj}}{\text{hyp}} = \dfrac{4.0}{5.0} = 0.8$, and $\dfrac{\text{opp}}{\text{adj}} = \dfrac{3.0}{4.0} = 0.75$. The values for the larger triangle are $\dfrac{\text{opp}'}{\text{hyp}'} = \dfrac{4.5}{7.5} = 0.6$, $\dfrac{\text{adj}'}{\text{hyp}'} = \dfrac{6.0}{7.5} = 0.8$, and $\dfrac{\text{opp}'}{\text{adj}'} = \dfrac{4.5}{6.0} = 0.75$. The relative lengths of the sides are therefore the same in triangles whose angles are the same.

{In fact, the relative lengths of the sides of a triangle are the same for *any* triangle that has the same angles as the triangles in Figure 8.4, however large or small the triangle is. But if we change the shape of the triangle, so that the angles are different, then the relative lengths of the sides of the triangle will be different from those you calculated above.}

Question 8.6   (a) sin 60° = 0.87; (b) cos 60° = 0.50; (c) tan 60° = 1.7; (d) cos 30° = 0.87; (e) cos 45° = 0.71; (f) sin 45° = 0.71; (g) sin 10° = 0.17; (h) cos 10° = 0.98; (i) tan 10° = 0.18; (j) tan 80° = 5.7.

Question 8.7   For both the graphs in Figure 8.7a and b, the gradient is measured as a 'rise' in y of 6.0 units, divided by a 'run' in x of 4.0 units. The gradient k in each case is therefore $\frac{6.0}{4.0} = 1.5$. In Figure 8.7a, when $x = 0$ then $y = 0$, so in this case $c = 0$ and the equation of this straight line is simply $y = 1.5x$. In Figure 8.7b, when $x = 0$ then $y = 2.0$, so here $c = 2.0$ and the equation of this straight line is $y = 1.5x + 2.0$.

Question 8.8   In Box 8.3 we showed what each of the terms in the equation of a straight line meant:

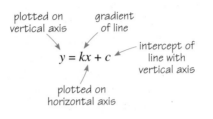

We can rearrange the equation $v = u + at$ so that it has a similar form, and each term then has a similar meaning:

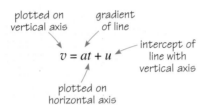

So a graph of v against t would have a gradient equal to a and the line would intercept the vertical axis at a point whose value is equal to u. The acceleration of the bus would therefore be given by the gradient of the graph, and its initial speed (at $t = 0$) by the intercept with the vertical (speed) axis.

Question 8.9   A graph of ΔE_g against Δh will be a straight line that passes through the origin. Since the equation of this straight line is $\Delta E_g = mg\Delta h$, the gradient of the graph will be equal to mg. So we have $mg = 0.019\,6 \, \text{kg m s}^{-2}$ and therefore

$$m = \frac{0.019\,6 \, \text{kg m s}^{-2}}{9.8 \, \text{m s}^{-2}} = 2.0 \times 10^{-3} \, \text{kg}$$

The mass of the locust is therefore 2.0 g.

{Notice here that the constant is in fact two values, m and g, multiplied together. But as both of these are constant, $m \times g$ will also be a constant.}

Question 8.10   (a) If there are 500 lines in 1 mm, then the spacing between the lines will be $\dfrac{1 \, \text{mm}}{500} = 0.002$ mm apart. Since $1 \, \mu\text{m} = 10^{-6}$ m, then $1 \, \mu\text{m} = 10^{-3}$ mm, so the spacing between the lines is 2 μm.

(b) A line spacing of 4 μm is equivalent to 0.004 mm, so there will be $\dfrac{1}{0.004 \, \text{mm}} = 250$ lines per mm.

Question 8.11   A grating that has *more* lines per mm ruled on its surface will have lines that are *closer together* than those of the original grating. So the line spacing d for grating B will be smaller than the line spacing for grating A. Since the spread of a diffraction pattern (characterized by $\sin\theta_n$) is *inversely* proportional to d (Equation 8.4), as d is reduced so the spread of the diffraction pattern will increase. The result of replacing grating A with grating B is therefore that the spots in the diffraction pattern will be *further apart* than before.

Question 8.12   (a) If the first order spots in the diffraction pattern produced by the new grating lie in the positions previously occupied by the fourth order spots produced by the original grating, these orders must have the same angles of diffraction. The value of $\sin\theta$ is therefore the same in each case, so the value of $\dfrac{n\lambda}{d}$ must also be the same. The wavelength is the same for both situations — only n and d are different. So, if n is four times smaller, then d must also be four times smaller to ensure that $\dfrac{n}{d}$ remains constant. The new grating therefore has a line spacing of $d = \dfrac{10\,\mu m}{4} = 2.5\,\mu m$.

(b) As above, the fact that the third order spots produced by the blue laser lie in the same positions as the second order spots produced by the red laser implies that these orders have the same angles of diffraction. In this case $\dfrac{n\lambda}{d}$ must be the same for each situation, and d is unchanged. Clearly then, $2\times\lambda_{red} = 3\times\lambda_{blue}$, which can be rearranged to give

$$\lambda_{blue} = \tfrac{2}{3}\lambda_{red} = \tfrac{2}{3}\times 660\,nm = 440\,nm$$

Question 8.13   (a) 1 kHz corresponds to 10^3 Hz, 1 MHz corresponds to 10^6 Hz, and 1 GHz corresponds to 10^9 Hz. {The first two of these occur within the radio wave part of the spectrum. The third is on the boundary between radio waves and microwaves.}

(b) 1 nm corresponds to 10^{-9} m and so should be marked on the wavelength axis somewhere between 3×10^{-10} m and 3×10^{-9} m. {This is near the boundary between the ultraviolet and X-ray parts of the spectrum.} 1 μm corresponds to 10^{-6} m and so should be marked on the wavelength axis somewhere between 3×10^{-7} m and 3×10^{-6} m. {This is in the infrared part of the spectrum, at a slightly longer wavelength than red light. (From the insert to Figure 8.9 you can see that the longest wavelength of visible radiation is about 7×10^{-7} m.)}

1 mm corresponds to 10^{-3} m and so should be written on the wavelength axis somewhere between 3×10^{-4} m and 3×10^{-3} m. {This is in the microwave part of the spectrum.}

Question 8.14   All electromagnetic radiation travels at the same speed, $c = 3.00\times 10^8$ m s^{-1}, and the speed is equal to the frequency of the radiation multiplied by its wavelength: $c = f\lambda$. Remember that the 'nano' in nanometres (nm) indicates 10^{-9} and that the 'giga' in gigahertz (GHz) indicates 10^9. So for the ray-gun, the speed of the radiation may be calculated as

$$(100\times 10^9\,s^{-1})\times(0.1\times 10^{-9}\,m) = 10\,m\,s^{-1}$$

Clearly, whatever 'rays' this gun emits, they are not electromagnetic radiation!

Question 8.15   (a) Rearranging Equation 8.2, $f = \dfrac{c}{\lambda}$. So in this case

$$f = \frac{3.00\times 10^8\,m\,s^{-1}}{1\,500\,m} = 2.00\times 10^5\,s^{-1} = 200\,kHz$$

The frequency for BBC Radio 4 longwave broadcasts is therefore 200 kHz.

(b) Rearranging Equation 8.2 again, $\lambda = \dfrac{c}{f}$. So in this case

$$\lambda = \frac{3.00\times 10^8\,m\,s^{-1}}{100\times 10^6\,Hz} = 3.00\,m$$

So the wavelength of a typical VHF broadcast is only a few metres.

Question 9.1   (a) One of the key results seen in the photoelectric effect is that the maximum kinetic energy of the photoelectrons depends on the frequency of the radiation that illuminates the metal surface (Figure 9.1b). Green light has a *higher* frequency than yellow light (see Figure 8.9), and so the maximum kinetic energy of the photoelectrons liberated by the green light is *higher* than the maximum kinetic energy of the photoelectrons liberated by the yellow light.

(b) The intensity of the illumination has *no effect* on the maximum kinetic energy of the photoelectrons that are liberated. All that happens when a more intense source of radiation is used is that *more* photoelectrons are liberated (Figure 9.1a), but with exactly the same range of energies as before.

Question 9.2 (a) Since ultraviolet radiation has a higher frequency than infrared radiation (see Figure 8.9), and the energy of a photon is proportional to the frequency of the radiation ($E_{ph} \propto f$), a photon of ultraviolet radiation must carry a greater amount of energy than a photon of infrared radiation.

(b) Since microwave radiation has a larger wavelength than light (see Figure 8.9), and the energy of a photon is inversely proportional to the wavelength of the radiation ($E_{ph} \propto \dfrac{1}{\lambda}$), a photon of light carries a greater amount of energy than a photon of microwave radiation.

Question 9.3 (a) One photon causes one electron to be liberated from the metal. The energy of the absorbed photon is divided between the energy needed to liberate the electron from the metal and the kinetic energy imparted to the photoelectron. So, in this case, the energy that was required to remove the electron from the metal is simply $(3.0 - 0.7)\,\text{eV} = 2.3\,\text{eV}$.

(b) In this second case, the kinetic energy imparted to the photoelectron is $(3.0 - 2.1)\,\text{eV} = 0.9\,\text{eV}$.

{In both cases, energy is conserved; the photon's energy is all transferred to an electron, and part of this energy is used to free the electron from the metal. The balance appears as the kinetic energy of the photoelectron.}

Question 9.4 Equation 9.2 may be rearranged to make λ the subject, namely $\lambda = \dfrac{hc}{E_{ph}}$, so in this case

$$\lambda = \frac{(4.1 \times 10^{-15}\ \text{eV Hz}^{-1}) \times (3.00 \times 10^8\ \text{m s}^{-1})}{511 \times 10^3\ \text{eV}}$$

$$= 2.4 \times 10^{-12}\ \text{m}$$

The wavelength of the radiation corresponding to the X-ray photon is therefore $2.4 \times 10^{-12}\,\text{m}$ which is equivalent to $0.002\,4\,\text{nm}$.

{Notice that the question gave the photon energy in units of kiloelectronvolts (keV) and so a factor of 10^3 appears in the calculation to convert the value into electronvolts (eV). Be careful to always note the prefixes for units when doing calculations.}

Question 9.5 The first thing to do is to convert the frequency of the radiation into the equivalent energy of each photon in electronvolts. Using Equation 9.1, $E_{ph} = hf = (4.1 \times 10^{-15}\ \text{eV Hz}^{-1}) \times (1.5 \times 10^{15}\ \text{Hz}) = 6.2\,\text{eV}$.

Now it's simply a matter of applying the law of conservation of energy as expressed by Equation 9.3, namely $E_{k,\,max} = E_{ph} - E_0 = (6.2 - 4.6)\,\text{eV} = 1.6\,\text{eV}$. So the maximum kinetic energy of the photoelectrons is $1.6\,\text{eV}$.

Question 9.6 (a) The photon energy corresponding to a wavelength of $150\,\text{nm}$ is given by Equation 9.2 as

$$E_{ph} = \frac{hc}{\lambda}$$

$$= \frac{(4.1 \times 10^{-15}\ \text{eV Hz}^{-1}) \times (3.00 \times 10^8\ \text{m s}^{-1})}{150 \times 10^{-9}\ \text{m}}$$

$$= 8.2\,\text{eV}$$

(b) Photons with an energy of $8.2\,\text{eV}$ cause electrons to be emitted whose maximum kinetic energy is $6.3\,\text{eV}$. So, using Equation 9.3, $E_{k,\,max} = E_{ph} - E_0$, conservation of energy shows that $6.3\,\text{eV} = 8.2\,\text{eV} - E_0$. Therefore $E_0 = 1.9\,\text{eV}$ for this metal. This is the minimum energy needed to eject electrons from the metal.

The wavelength of radiation corresponding to photons that have this energy is obtained by applying Equation 9.2 again. This time

$$\lambda = \frac{hc}{E_0}$$

$$= \frac{(4.1 \times 10^{-15}\ \text{eV Hz}^{-1}) \times (3.00 \times 10^8\ \text{m s}^{-1})}{1.9\,\text{eV}}$$

$$= 6.5 \times 10^{-7}\ \text{m}$$

The wavelength of radiation corresponding to the lowest energy photons that can free electrons from the metal is therefore about $650\,\text{nm}$, in the visible (red) part of the spectrum.

(c) Since infrared radiation has a longer wavelength than visible radiation (light), the energy of photons of infrared radiation is less than $1.9\,\text{eV}$ and therefore these photons have insufficient energy to free electrons from the metal.

Question 10.1 (a) Since the electrons in the beam all have the same energy, they all have the same wavelength. The diffraction grating will diffract this beam of electrons, and the diffraction pattern produced on the screen will consist of a series of diffraction orders. This will look rather like the patterns produced by the laser beams in Activity 8.1 (see Figure 8.8).

(b) If the electrons in the beam had a range of energies, and therefore a range of effective wavelengths, then each order of the diffraction pattern would be dispersed into a 'spectrum' of electron wavelengths.

Index

Entries and page numbers in **bold type** refer to key words which are printed in **bold** in the text and which are defined in the Glossary. These are terms that we expect you to be able to explain the meaning of, and use correctly, both during and at the end of the course. An entry followed by ^{G} indicates a term which is defined in the Glossary but which is not bold in the text. Where the page number is given in *italics*, the indexed information is carried mainly or wholly in an illustration or table. Answers to questions are not indexed.

Acknowledgements

Grateful acknowledgement is made to the following sources for permission to reproduce material in this block:

Figures

Figures 1.1, 3.4, 3.13 and 4.3: Science & Society Picture Library; *Figure 1.4a*: Celestron International; *Figure 1.4b*: Courtesy of Professor K. Seddon and Dr T. Evans, Queen's University Belfast/Science Photo Library; *Figure 1.4c*: National Optical Astronomy Observatories; *Figure 2.1b*: Courtesy of Gordon Garradd/Science Photo Library; *Figure 2.7*: Hulton Picture Library; *Figure 3.7*: Courtesy of Corbis/Bettmann; *Figure 8.1*: Images Colour Library Ltd; *Figure 10.1*: Courtesy of Ullarwin Bilderdienst; *Figure 10.2a*: Courtesy of Naomi Williams and Goodfellow.

Title page photograph

Courtesy of IBM Corporation, Research Division, Almaden Research Center.